Intelligence as Adaptive Behavior

An Experiment in
Computational Neuroethology

Perspectives in Artificial Intelligence

Volume 6

Editor:

B. Chandrasekaran

Ohio State University
Columbus, Ohio

Editorial Advisory Board:

Rodney A. Brooks

Massachusetts Institute of Technology
Cambridge, Massachusetts

Kenneth Forbus

University of Illinois, Urbana-Champaign
Urbana, Illinois

Mark Fox

Carnegie Mellon University
Pittsburgh, Pennsylvania

Charles Rich

Massachusetts Institute of Technology
Cambridge, Massachusetts

Robert Wilensky

University of California, Berkeley
Berkeley, California

Intelligence as Adaptive Behavior

An Experiment in Computational Neuroethology

Randall D. Beer

Department of Computer Engineering and Science
Case Western Reserve University
Cleveland, Ohio

ACADEMIC PRESS, INC.
Harcourt Brace Jovanovich, Publishers
Boston   San Diego   New York
London   Sydney   Tokyo   Toronto

Copyright © 1990 by Academic Press, Inc.
All rights reserved.
No part of this publication may be reproduced or
transmitted in any form or by any means, electronic
or mechanical, including photocopy, recording, or
any information storage and retrieval system, without
permission in writing from the publisher.

ACADEMIC PRESS, INC.
1250 Sixth Avenue, San Diego, CA 92101

United Kingdom Edition published by
ACADEMIC PRESS LIMITED
24-28 Oval Road, London NW1 7DX

Library of Congress Cataloging-in-Publication Data

Beer, Randall D.
    Intelligence as adaptive behavior : an experiment in computational
neuroethology / Randall D. Beer.
        p.   cm. — (Perspectives in artificial intelligence ; v.6)
    Revision of thesis (Ph.D.) — Case Western Reserve University,
1989.
    Includes bibliographical references and index.
    ISBN 0-12-084730-2 (alk. paper)
    1. Animal behavior—Computer simulation.   2. Nervous system-
Insects—Computer simulation.   3. Artificial intelligence.
4. Adaptation (Biology)—Computer simulation.   I. Title.
II. Series: Perspectives in artificial intelligence ; vol.6.
QL757.65.D37B44   1990
591.5'1'0113—dc20   90-35924
                                                              CIP

Printed in the United States of America
90   91   92   93   9 8 7 6 5 4 3 2 1

To my family:

Sherry, Michelle, and Brian
and
Pat, Kenneth, and Laura

Editor's Note

Despite the fact that artificial intelligence (AI) lacks a unified methodology, until recently there has been at least one idea that was shared almost universally among all schools within AI: that intelligence is a process of manipulating representations of the world and ideas. Even more specifically, the representations were understood as discrete symbolic in character, i.e., symbols of the type used by Turing Machines, and the mechanisms of intelligence were assumed to be algorithmic.

Two distinct visions have motivated the AI enterprise, even though in practice most AI researchers didn't (and still generally don't) think of these two visions as potentially different: one idea, epitomized by the Turing test, is that of capturing the pure essence of intelligence as a disembodied representational system; the other, the idea of making a robot that sees, hears, talks, and perhaps even feels, and has a body, is captured by the R2-D2s and HALs of moviedom. But in fact, except for an occasional foray into the integrated robot world, AI has largely followed the Turing dream. The reason most AI researchers have not seen any inherent conflict in the two visions is because of the assumption that the way to build robots is to create a representation-processing thinking machine with sensors at one end and actuators at the other end. By this view, thought is disembodied. Sensors supply the representation of the world, and these representations are processed, resulting in additional representations that correspond to instructions to be sent to the actuators.

Interestingly, this "pure thought as symbol manipulation" view was applied not only to problems that are essentially symbolic manipulation in character, such as theorem proving, but also to problems that had to do with the robot's own body, such as planning movements of its body parts, or to phenomena in which sensory interaction with the world was very important. Some researchers have suspected that perhaps the problem was being made more, rather than less, complex by emphasizing the orthodox centralized symbol-processing models. Attacks on the orthodox view have come from three directions:

i. Non-Representational Approaches

Perhaps much of intelligent action does not require or use explicit representations and their processing. For example, a coin-sorter, such as the one that is used in most soda-dispensing machines, uses levers and slots that respond differently to the weights and diameters of various coins. This physical mechanism enables the sorter to identify the coins. A representational language is useful to *describe* the machine: a stage in the operation of the sorter can be understood by a statement such as, "At this point the system uses the weight to decide if the coin is a dime or a quarter." Representation thus may be a meta-language to talk about the phenomena involved rather than a literal occurrence. In perception, Gibson has long been associated with the idea of "direct" perception, a view that eschews representation processing in favor of direct mappings from sensory information to categorical perception, mappings that arise directly from the architecture of the system. Connectionism has been embraced warmly by many philosophers on the grounds that it provides such a non-representational account of cognition. However, it can be argued that connectionism is as representational as the traditional symbolic systems, the major difference being the type of representation. (See B. Chandrasekaran, A. Goel and D. Allemang, 1989). Edelman has argued similarly that the neural matter should not be modeled as a representation processor but as something whose connectivity patterns get selected over trials: the neurons form connections, the successful connections are retained, and the unsuccessful ones stop contributing to decisions.

ii. Reactive Approaches

For many tasks, the appropriate architecture for producing solutions is one that is "reactive," i.e., the responses are indexed directly over the situation description, rather than resulting from complex problem solving using abstract world models. In real-world cognitive agents, in particular, the evolution of sensory apparatus is such that most actions are indexed directly by sensory abstractions. As actions are taken, the changes in the world are monitored directly and additional steps are taken reactively as well. A pioneer in this method of organizing robot action planning is Jappinen (1979), who built a system in my own laboratory for perception-directed skill learning that learned to navigate paths in a simulated world. The work of Agre and Chapman (1987) is a more recent example of an approach that uses perception-directed reactive actions as a way of responding to a complex environment without complex planning.

iii. Distributed Approaches

A third direction of attack involves some aspects of i and ii, but adds yet another twist. Not only may there be no need for complex symbolic processing on representations of world models, but the action generation may not be performed centrally at all. Brooks (1986) has articulated an approach for robot motion planning in which reactiveness of responses is combined with distribution of action-generation in a subsumption architecture.

Two books in the Series now arrive which show some of the best work in this new genre of AI research. Since they have interesting philosophical underpinnings in common, this Editor's Note serves as an introduction to both.

Jon Connell's book, *Minimalist Mobile Robotics: A Colony-style Architecture for an Artificial Creature*, is written in the direction described in iii: the robot has no central world models, but a set of distributed, local partial models are coordinated in a subsumption architecture to achieve the robot's goals in the physical world. Randy Beer's book, *Intelligence as Adaptive Behavior: An Experiment in Computational Neuroethology*, abandons the traditional AI goal of simulating the highly symbolic, linguistic and logical behaviors of human intelligence, and concentrates instead on understanding how simple nervous systems show complex adaptive behavior in dealing with a dynamic environment. His thesis is that high-level symbolic behavior should eventually be shown to be built on top of this adaptive organism, rather than as a completely separate logic or symbolic engine that merely monitors and controls the sensors and the body. Connell and Beer share a world view about the importance of moving away from the centralized model-manipulation paradigm of traditional AI.

The Perspectives in Artificial Intelligence Series sets for itself a goal of presenting works that point to or exploit interesting and provocative new directions in artificial intelligence. These two books eminently qualify under this criterion.

— B. Chandrasekaran

References

P. E. Agre and D. A. Chapman (1987). Pengi: an implementation of a theory of activity. In *Proceedings of the Sixth National Conference on Artificial Intelligence*, pp. 268-272.

R. A. Brooks (1986). A robust layered control system for a mobile robot. *IEEE Journal of Robotics and Automation*, **RA-2/1**, March, 14-23.

B. Chandrasekaran, A. Goel and D. Allemang (1989). Connectionism and information processing abstractions: the message still counts more than the medium. *AI Magazine*, **9:4**, 24-34.

H. Jappinen (1979). A perception-based developmental skill acquisition system. Ph. D. Dissertation, The Ohio State University.

Contents

Preface

For over thirty years, thinking about thinking has been dominated by the notion that intelligence consists largely of the proper manipulation of symbolic representations of the world. This conception of intelligence has its roots in a literal application of the metaphor of computation to our introspections on human reasoning. Within AI, it has led to an almost exclusive preoccupation with modeling isolated cognitive skills within relatively narrow task domains.

There is no doubt that this ideology has been widely influential, nor that it has produced some notable technological success stories. Within AI today, however, there is a growing sense of disillusionment with this approach. The "intelligence" exhibited so far by current AI systems is extremely narrow and brittle, depending for its success upon a careful circumscription of the problem domain. Early expectations have not been met, and it is not at all clear that we are any closer to a deep understanding of intelligent behavior than we were thirty years ago. AI practitioners have even begun to question some of the philosophical assumptions underlying the notion of mental representation itself. The field's deep dissatisfaction is perhaps nowhere more apparent than in the speed with which the few alternative paradigms that have arisen, such as connectionism, have been embraced. This despite the fact that these alternatives often have serious limitations of their own.

This book has two goals. First, it argues for a view of intelligence which is somewhat different from the traditional one. Rather than focusing on the apparently uniquely human skills of language and logical reasoning, I wish

to emphasize instead the more universal ability of animals to cope continuously with the complex, dynamic, unpredictable world in which they live.
To me, this penchant for *adaptive behavior* is the essence of intelligence:
the ability of an autonomous agent to flexibly adjust its behavioral repertoire to the moment-to-moment contingencies which arise in its interaction
with its environment. Our higher cognitive functions are our own particular human elaborations of this more fundamental capability, and are deeply
inseparable from it.

The second goal of this book is to explore a particular methodology
for the construction of autonomous agents. In order to address some of
the shortcomings of the classical methodology, the explicit use of symbolic
representations is avoided. Instead, I focus on achieving the appropriate dynamics of interaction between an agent and its environment. This methodology is founded on the idea that even simpler natural animals possess a
degree of adaptive behavior which far exceeds that of any artificial system.
In addition, the neurobiological mechanisms underlying the behavior of simpler animals are beginning to be worked out in some detail. The essence of
my approach, called *computational neuroethology*, lies in the direct use of
behavioral and neurobiological ideas from simpler natural animals to construct artificial nervous systems for controlling the behavior of autonomous
agents.

The bulk of this book describes a particular experiment in computational neuroethology. A simulated insect is developed whose behavior is
controlled by an artificial nervous system. The design of this artificial
insect is based in part upon specific behaviors and neural circuits drawn
from several natural animals. Its behavioral repertoire includes locomotion,
wandering, edge-following, and feeding. In addition, the insect exhibits a
behavioral hierarchy, which allows it to continuously synthesize behavior
appropriate to its changing internal and external environment. Several behavioral characteristics of this simulated insect bear a striking resemblance
to those of natural animals.

Quite apart from its interest as an autonomous agent, the artificial insect offers a unique opportunity to experiment with the design of neural
circuitry. Despite the well-known fact that nervous systems consist of very
specific architectures containing nerve cells with a variety of spatiotem-
porally complex response properties, most of the artificial neural network
architectures which have been explored are uniform collections of simple
processing units with a regular interconnection scheme. The construction

of the artificial insect's nervous system has allowed me to explore the application of a number of neurobiological principles to the design of heterogeneous neural networks. To the extent that some of our neural circuit designs remain sufficiently faithful to the neurobiology that inspired them, there is also the possibility of applying insights gained from the simulated insect to the understanding of natural nervous systems.

The artificial insect developed in this book is not intended as a final solution to the narrow and inflexible character of current AI systems. Rather, it is an initial volley in what I think will be a very long game. The sort of explicit interaction that I am advocating between the neuroethology of simpler animals and AI is long overdue, and there is a great deal of work to be done. The construction of entire nervous systems for controlling the behavior of complete autonomous agents is not a task which has been seriously attempted before. The artificial insect is best viewed as an attempt to define the important questions raised by this methodology, and to explore some initial models. Despite its preliminary character, however, this insect exhibits a number of important similarities to the adaptive behavior of natural animals. In addition, it raises for serious discussion such fundamental questions as what role the notion of representation actually plays in the construction, behavior, and description of an autonomous agent.

A Guide for the Reader

This book covers a great deal of territory, from the foundations of AI to invertebrate neurobiology. Because the computational neuroethology approach requires this broad perspective, I strongly encourage a complete reading of the book. As a guidepost to readers with more specific interests, however, a brief description of the contents of each chapter follows.

In Chapter 1, the foundations of the approach advocated in this book are described. An attempt is made to characterize the assumptions underlying the classical AI methodology. I argue that the inability of current AI systems to handle unconstrained interaction with the real world can be traced to limitations inherent in the methodology itself. The notions of *adaptive behavior* and *computational neuroethology* are defined, and I argue that a careful study and modeling of the biological mechanisms of adaptive behavior in simpler natural animals can lead to important insights into the design of flexible intelligent agents. Finally, an overview of the artificial insect developed in this book is then provided.

Chapter 2 introduces some of the basic concepts of animal behavior and neurobiology, with a particular emphasis on those aspects that have a direct bearing on the design of the artificial insect. This biological background is important for understanding both the overall flavor of computational neuroethology and the specific details of the simulated insect.

Chapter 3 describes the overall design of the artificial insect in some detail. The physical models utilized for its body and environment are discussed. Next, the model neurons used in the artificial insect's nervous system are described. This neural model is compared and contrasted with existing neural network models. The implementation and user interface of the simulation are then discussed. Finally, a brief overview of related work is provided.

In Chapter 4, a distributed heterogeneous neural network for hexapod locomotion is developed. This controller is directly inspired by the literature on insect locomotion. The chapter demonstrates that the locomotion controller can generate a variety of statically stable gaits simply by varying the steady activity of a single neuron. The neuroethological implications of this circuit for insect locomotion are discussed, and it is compared with existing distributed hexapod locomotion controllers.

Chapter 5 raises the question of how heterogeneous neural networks can be analyzed. The use of *lesion studies* (i.e., examining the behavioral effects of selective damage to a neural controller) for this purpose is explored. This technique is applied to the locomotion controller presented in Chapter 4; several interesting results regarding its operation and robustness are described. The implications of these results for both artificial neural networks and natural nervous systems are discussed briefly.

In Chapter 6, neural controllers for wandering, recoil, and edge-following are presented. These behaviors allow the insect to explore its environment autonomously. While the neural circuits for these behaviors are only loosely based upon neurobiological data, they raise a number of important issues in the design of heterogeneous neural networks for the adaptive control of behavior, including the neural implementation of extended, temporally patterned responses to brief stimuli.

Chapter 7 presents a neural controller for feeding. This is the first real example of goal-oriented problem-solving in the artificial insect, and thus the first opportunity to examine the neural integration of goal-oriented planning with reactive responses. Like the locomotion controller, the design of the feeding circuitry is based in part upon specific neurobiological data.

This chapter demonstrates that certain characteristics of the artificial insect's feeding behavior bear a striking resemblance to the feeding behavior of natural animals. The neuroethological implications of these results are considered briefly.

Chapter 8 addresses the problem of behavioral choice. When multiple, conflicting behaviors are potentially appropriate in a given situation, the insect must have some means of choosing among them. These interactions among behaviors add additional complexities to the design of the underlying neural controllers. This chapter describes the neural implementation of a behavioral hierarchy for the artificial insect, and demonstrates the dynamic reconfiguration of this hiearachy in response to a simple maze problem in the insect's environment.

Chapter 9 discusses a number of issues which have been raised by this research, including some of its implications for AI, robotics, neural networks, and neuroscience.

Appendices A and B provide considerably more detail on the physical models and neural controllers, respectively, than is available in the main text.

Acknowledgements

This book is a substantially revised version of my Ph.D. dissertation, which was presented to the Department of Computer Engineering and Science at Case Western Reserve University in July, 1989.

No research occurs in either an intellectual or personal vacuum. It has been a very long haul from my original sketchy ideas to the publication of this book. I would like to acknowledge the contributions to that process of the following people, and offer all of them my deepest gratitude.

I thank Hillel Chiel and Leon Sterling, advisors, colleagues, and friends, who have influenced my research in ways both large and small. Hillel taught me to appreciate the biological details, as well as most of the neuroscience I know, and kept my simplifications as honest as possible. He has also made numerous specific contributions to this project, including spearheading the lesion studies of the locomotion controller, providing ideas for neural controller designs and suggestions for the simulation user interface, and proposing that I start with insect locomotion in the first place. Hillel is one of those rare individuals who make crossing disciplinary boundaries appear almost effortless. Leon has a deep understanding of the foundations of artificial intelligence, and my ideas have been clarified in many long discussions with him. Leon also encouraged me to follow my instincts, and yet was instrumental in keeping this research on track. Both Hillel and Leon spent more time on this project than I had any right to expect, and consistently gave me as much rope as I needed to pursue my ideas while somehow managing to prevent me from ever hanging myself with it.

Yoh-Han Pao created and directed the Center for Automation and Intelligent Systems Research, which provided an excellent research environment within which to work. Time and again he supplied the resources and financial and political support I required with very few strings attached, as well as endless encouragement and good advice.

I would like to thank Humberto Maturana, Francisco Varela, Terry Winograd, Rodney Brooks, Greg Hood, and Philip Agre, whose ideas have had a profound influence on the direction of my research.

Kamal Hathi, Ümit Yalçinalp, Philip Schaefer, Işil Bozma, David Helman, and others have, over the years, patiently listened to my sometimes crazy ideas and helped to clarify them. In addition to Mark Guzowski, Jim Vezina, Myungsook Klassen, Farrokh Khatibi, Georges Zwinglestein, Dejan Sobajic, Larry Boyd and many others, they made the Center a fun place to work.

Sari Kalin and the rest of the crew at Academic Press made the process of producing a book surprisingly painless. In addition, I would like to thank Leon and Hillel, as well as two anonymous reviewers, for making a number of critical comments on earlier drafts of this book which considerably improved its organization. Of course, I take full responsibility for the final form and content.

Finally, I would like to thank my wife, Sherry, whose patience, love and understanding know no bounds. Along with my children, Michelle and Brian, my parents, Pat and Kenneth, and my sister Laura, my family has been an endless source of encouragement, support, resources, and just plain love.

Randall D. Beer
Case Western Reserve University
Cleveland, Ohio

List of Figures

Chapter 1

Foundations

1.1 Introduction

What does it mean, to be intelligent? What are the mechanisms which underlie intelligent behavior? How can intelligent behavior be simulated or reproduced on a computer? These are the questions which define the field of artificial intelligence. The first question is inherited from the philosophy of mind. The second question is a principal concern of cognitive science. The third question, however, is uniquely its own. As much as the questions themselves characterize the AI endeavor, their conventional answers determine its daily practice. This chapter attempts to characterize, and criticize, these conventional answers, and to propose alternatives whose exploration will concern us throughout the remainder of this book.

1.2 The Traditional View

1.2.1 Intelligence as Deliberative Reasoning

What does it mean, to be intelligent? The human capacity for language and abstract reasoning is generally considered to be the hallmark of intelligence. There is a long philosophical tradition which venerates human knowledge and rationality as those attributes which make us most uniquely human. On this traditional view, intelligence is largely equated with *deliberative reasoning*, by which I mean the ability to consciously reason through a problem. Playing a good game of chess, proving a mathematical theorem, designing an airplane, negotiating a peace treaty — these things require intelligence. In contrast, assembling a bicycle or crossing a busy street is not usually considered to require a great deal of intelligence; skill perhaps, even cunning, but not intelligence. Intelligence is uniquely associated with the mind, with thinking. It is what enables one to succeed in intellectual endeavors, such as those encountered in a typical academic setting.

1.2.2 Deliberative Reasoning as Computation

What are the mechanisms which underlie intelligent behavior? The traditional answer to this question is largely drawn from introspection on conscious human reasoning. Essentially the same process by which we deliberately reason through, say, an anagram is hypothesized to underlie all intelligent behavior. Since its inception, the central dogma of the cognitive sciences has been that that process involves the appropriate manipulation of mental representations of the world (Stillings *et al.*, 1987; Gardner, 1985). Typically, these representations are viewed as linguistic symbols which stand for the real-world entities that they represent, and their manipulations are viewed as a species of computation (Pylyshyn, 1984; Fodor, 1975).

This idea has appeared under a great variety of names, including the *Representation Hypothesis* (Winograd and Flores, 1986), the *Physical Symbol System Hypothesis* (Newell and Simon, 1976), the *Representational Theory of Mind* (Stich, 1983), the *Information Processing Paradigm* (Reed, 1982), and the *Knowledge Representation Hypothesis* (Smith, 1985). There are, of course, many technical differences between the research programs carried out under these various banners. However, at their core is a common vision about the mechanisms underlying intelligent behavior. With characteristic wit, Dennett has summarized the basic tenets of this approach (which he refers to as "High Church Computationalism") as follows (Dennett, 1986, pp. 60-61):

> (1) *Thinking is information processing.* That is, the terms of folk psychology are to be spruced up by the theorist and recast more rigorously: "thinking" will be analyzed into an amalgam of processes ("inference" and "problem solving" and "search" and so forth); "seeing" and "hearing" will be analyzed in terms of "perceptual analysis" which itself will involve inference, hypothesis-testing strategies, and the like.

(2) *Information processing is computation (which is symbol manipulation).* The information-processing systems and operations will themselves be analyzed in terms of processes of "computation," and since, as Fodor says, "no computation without representation," a medium of representation is posited, consisting of *symbols* belonging to a *system* which has a *syntax* (formation rules) and *formal rules of symbol manipulation* for deriving new symbolic complexes from old.

(3) the semantics of these symbols connects thinking to the external world. For instance, some brain-thingamabob (brain state, brain event, complex property of brain tissue) will be the symbol for MIT, and some other brain thingamabob will be the symbol for budget. Then we will be able to determine that another, composite brain-thingamabob refers to the MIT budget, since the symbolic structures composable within the representational medium have interpretations that are a systematic function of the semantic interpretation of their elements. In other words, there is a language of thought, and many of the terms of this language (many of the symbols manipulated during computation) can be said to *refer* to things in the world such as Chicago, whales, and the day after tomorrow.

It is difficult to overestimate the impact that this representation hypothesis (as I shall call it) has had on cognitive science in general and AI in particular. Some might argue that AI *is* the representation hypothesis. Like any scientific paradigm, it has colored the way we define the very phenomena we seek to understand. Under the rubric of this hypothesis, perception *is* the construction of internal representations of the external environment. Learning *is* the modification of existing representations and the accumulation of new ones. Memory *is* the storage and retrieval of representations. Language *is* the encoding, exchange, and decoding of representations. Reasoning *is* the logical manipulation of representations. Taking action *is* the execution of a representation of the plan of action to be performed.

Its ubiquity notwithstanding, we must remember that the representation hypothesis is only an hypothesis, yet to be shown either true or false. As Rorty says, "Ideas in the mind are no more or less disreputable than neurons in the brain, mitochondria in the cells, passions in the soul, or moral progress in history" (1979, p. 209). Like any way of talking about the world, the notion of manipulating mental representations is undeniably useful in some circumstances and quite useless in others.

The language of mental representations certainly accords rather well with our common sense explanations of human behavior, so-called "Folk Psychology." We regularly invoke such mental entities as beliefs, desires, ideas, and perceptions to rationalize human action. Why did John open the refrigerator door? Because he *wanted* something to eat and, since he *saw* the refrigerator standing there in the corner and *believed* that there was food in it, he *decided* to walk over and open the door.

However, the fact that a particular way of talking about the world is useful under some circumstances does not necessarily imply that it is a valid scientific explanation. The history of science is filled with folk theories that were wrong (Churchland, 1986). "Common sense tells me that the ground beneath my feet is flat and that the sun and moon circle overhead. It tells me that running faster will not make me shorter in the direction I run, or make my watch slow down. Common sense is full of generalizations which work over some limited (and common) range of phenomena, but which have to be abandoned when we go further" (Winograd, 1987a, p. 3).

The important question to ask about the representation hypothesis is not whether it is intuitively obvious or fundamentally flawed. Instead, we must determine the circumstances under which it provides a sufficient explanation, and ask whether or not it can account for the full range of phenomena that we associate with intelligent behavior. This is a question which can only be settled by empirical investigation, by actually applying the notion of symbol manipulation to instances of intelligent behavior and critically evaluating the results. Such is the nature of the AI endeavor.

1.2.3   The Classical AI Methodology

How can intelligent behavior be simulated or reproduced on a computer? Needless to say, the phenomena comprising human intelligence are enormously complex. As in any scientific or technological endeavor, progress requires that some simplifications be made. This need to simplify, coupled with the representation hypothesis and the characterization of intelligence as deliberative thinking, have produced what I will call the *classical methodology* for AI research. This methodology focuses on modeling the performance of human reasoning in restricted task domains as computations involving symbolic representations of the problem to be solved.

An application of the classical methodology generally proceeds as follows (Winograd and Flores, 1986). The first, and most important, step is to carefully circumscribe the intelligent behavior to be modeled. This is accomplished by identifying the knowledge which is important to the performance of the desired task in the given domain, and by characterizing its properties and interrelationships. The end result of this step is a *systematic domain*: a linguistic abstraction of the actual task and domain. This description is then encoded into a formal representation in which every relevant aspect can be explicitly stated as combinations of a finite number of representational primitives. In addition, the task to be performed must be expressible as the manipulation of elements of this representation. Finally, this formal representation is embedded in a computer program which actually carries out the required manipulations in such a way as to perform the desired task. Much of the actual work in AI lies in designing formal systems capable of adequately representing the required knowledge in a way which can be efficiently manipulated.

This methodology is pervasive in AI. It is, of course, true of all expert systems, which attempt to capture the knowledge and reasoning processes by which human experts solve problems in specialized technical domains. However, it also describes most work in such areas as planning, problem-solving, natural language understanding, and learning. To a large extent, it also applies to most of the AI work in vision, speech recognition, and robotics. The traditional AI approach to all of these phenomena has been to abstract systematic domains within which symbolic representations of the relevant concepts and their properties can be explicitly encoded and manipulated in ways which mimic human reasoning within the domain of interest.

The working assumptions embodied in the classical AI methodology can be summarized as follows: (1) most intelligent behavior can be modeled on the exemplar of conscious deliberation; (2) deliberative human reasoning is essentially a species of computation over symbolic representations of the world; (3) insights gained from modeling the performance of particular aspects of intelligence in restricted domains will eventually be synthesized into an understanding of generally intelligent behavior in unconstrained interaction with the real world.

1.3 An Empirical Critique

Attempts to mechanize human reasoning have been going on for hundreds of years. The idea of computational models of intelligence has been around as long as the idea of computation itself. The classical AI methodology has been pursued in essentially its modern form for over thirty years. What is the empirical status of this research program? What has actually been accomplished, what has proven to be most difficult, and what, if anything, can be learned from its pattern of successes and failures?

By many accounts, the AI research program is faring very well indeed. The number of AI researchers is at an all-time high. AI systems now play master level chess, solve difficult problems in mathematics, and converse in stylized but impressive natural language. Numerous commercially successful AI systems are in existence, solving a variety of problems of great practical importance. In fact, some AI techniques are becoming a standard part of computer science. On the scientific front, many fragments of intelligent behavior have now been simulated. Computer models of such diverse cognitive processes as memory, story understanding, and discovery are being explored. These models have provided important insights into the strengths and weaknesses of proposed theories of mind, and in some cases have generated experimentally testable hypotheses. To be sure, human cognition has turned out to be extraordinarily more difficult to understand and model than originally conceived, and many fundamental technical issues remain unresolved. Nevertheless, a steady stream of fresh ideas is entering the field, and progress continues to be made.

However, despite these external signs of progress, there has nevertheless been a growing undercurrent of frustration and disappointment within AI. The "intelligence" of AI systems is notoriously narrow and brittle. AI systems have not scaled well beyond the relatively limited domains to which they have been successfully applied. Their performance is extremely sensitive to the representational choices made by their designers, and brittle in the face of inevitable deviations of the real world from these abstractions. They are incapable of flexibly coping with contingencies not explicitly foreseen by their designers. In short, despite the fact that AI systems can outperform many human beings in certain technical domains, "we don't know how to build a program with the common sense of a dog" (Ed Fredkin, quoted in Winograd, 1987c).

These problems are widely recognized in AI today, but there is a common conviction that they stem only from temporary technical limitations which will eventually be overcome (Stefik and Bobrow, 1987). The exploration of techniques for addressing these limitations is currently an active area of AI research. Candidate solutions include the development of more sophisticated forms of logic (McCarthy, 1988), the rejection of logic in general (McDermott, 1987; Minsky, 1985), explicitly encoding large amounts of commonsense knowledge about the world (Lenat *et al.*, 1986; Hobbs and Moore, 1985), and the use of massively parallel models of computation (Hillis, 1985; Rumelhart and McClelland, 1986; Waltz, 1988).

This technological optimism is not universal, however. Indeed, to some observers, the limitations of current AI systems are symptomatic of a deeper problem with the representation hypothesis itself (Winograd and Flores, 1986; Brooks, 1987; Dreyfus and Dreyfus, 1988; Suchman, 1987; Maturana and Varela, 1980; Reeke and Edelman, 1988; Lakoff, 1987). These critics argue that, in attempting to explicitly articulate and encode the totality of human knowledge, AI is tackling precisely the sort of epistemological project that philosophers have been grappling with for thousands of years, without notable success. The reason for this failure, in the critics' view, is very simple: no fixed, objective, universal description of the world exists, and therefore none is available for encoding into formal representations in an AI system.

Rather, the "knowledge" that AI researchers seek to represent consists of linguistic abstractions, made in the context of a given conversation for a particular purpose. Such descriptions have no absolute existence, and certainly do not reflect an objective reality. For example, just because I may refer to John Doe as a liberal in the context of a given conversation does not mean that **liberal(JohnDoe)** is some objective fact about the world. This may be a perfectly legitimate characterization for some purposes and completely inaccurate for others. Freezing such a description into a formal representation is an attempt to decontextualize a statement that is fundamentally context sensitive. Any system whose operation is based upon such a representation is fundamentally inflexible, because it risks the possibility of breaking down in any situation other than the original context in which the description was valid.

Winograd (1987a) illustrates the essential difficulty with the following scenario. Suppose that the procedure for admitting new students to the Computer Science Department of some university is as follows. There is a collection of folders, one for each candidate. The contents of the folders consist of statements such as "Brown has a 4.6 GPA in his major," "Smith is a top athlete," and "Frankly, Jones is a first-class nincompoop." The admissions committee carries on a conversation in which further statements are made, such as "Brown is our top candidate," and ultimately sends

acceptance and rejection letters. What sorts of knowledge would need to
be represented by an AI system designed to aid in this admissions process?

> To take the most seemingly straightforward [example], we could
> have an entry for each student's GPA, and another for "GPA-
> in-major." But what counts as "in the major?" What objective
> real property is being measured here? Some schools might count
> all courses offered by the major department, others count those
> courses required for the major, etc. Some schools might have a
> "computer hardware engineering" major, while others give de-
> grees to computer specialists whose major is "mathematics."
> The point is not that these complexities are incomprehensible
> or could not be reduced to further distinctions. But when they
> are conglomerated into a single "property" (as they ultimately
> must be represented in a data representation or logical formal-
> ism), these distinctions are lost. The process of further dis-
> tinctions is potentially endless (what distinguishes a "computer
> science" course?). All hope is lost when we get to assigning each
> student an appropriate data base entry for his or her "class" of
> "nincompoopity." (Winograd, 1987a, p. 3)

And this is not an isolated problem. The literature abounds with examples of seemingly straightforward concepts and properties whose mean-
ings simply cannot be pinned down in isolation from the contexts of their
use, such as "bachelor," "lemon," "tiger," "bird," "water," "cup," and
"widow" (Winograd, 1985). The essential problem here is that behind
every statement (e.g. "Brown has a 4.6 GPA in his major") there is an
enormous set of unarticulated background assumptions. If an interpreta-
tional problem arises in the course of a given conversation, the participants
may be forced into further discussions concerning such things as the computation of grades at a particular university. However, no such further
discussions are possible for an AI system which explicitly represents the
fact **gpa_in_major(Brown, 4.6)**.

This problem offers a potential explanation for the following observation: the success of an AI system appears to be strongly correlated with
the degree to which its problem domain can be treated as an abstract mi-
croworld which is disconnected from the world at large (Dreyfus, 1979). AI
systems do reasonably well in such highly specialized domains as chess playing and symbolic integration precisely because the relevant facts about these

domains can be exhaustively and explicitly represented in a way which is largely isolated from our commonsense background knowledge of the world. There is no matter of interpretation as to what constitutes a legal chess move or an applicable integration formula.

In contrast, such tasks as story understanding or medical diagnosis are not so easily isolated from our commonsense background knowledge of the world. The success of AI systems on such more realistic tasks depends upon the extent to which cartoon-like caricatures of these tasks can be defined. MYCIN, for example, is a well-known expert system which reduces a doctor's ability to recommend courses of treatment for his patients to the "problem domain" of relating a fixed set of symptoms to a fixed set of bacterial infections, both of which are predefined by the programmer. Imagine the response of such a system to a broken arm, a gunshot wound, or a hypochondriac. Winograd has likened the resulting AI systems to bureaucracies, with their attendant inflexibility and brittleness (Winograd, 1987b).

"Look," goes the standard response to this line of criticism. "Of course an AI system intended for one problem domain won't automatically handle another. What does that prove? The required knowledge can always be added if necessary. AI studies intelligent behavior in the context of specific tasks in order to abstract general principles which will apply across all problem domains." This response is essentially a restatement of the simplifying assumption of the classical methodology, and a reaffirmation of the belief that the resulting patchwork of competencies will eventually be stitched into the quilt of generally intelligent behavior. This is precisely the belief that motivates such work as Lenat's CYC project, which is attempting to explicitly represent all of the knowledge contained in a small pocket encyclopedia (Lenat *et al.*, 1986).

But, and here is the crucial point, *what reason do we have for believing that such a synthesis is possible?* Philosophical issues aside, there is certainly no empirical evidence for this claim. While a great many AI *techniques* have indeed generalized across multiple problem domains, the representations upon which they operate have not. Rather, each new problem domain has required its own idiosyncratic way of representing the world, which is handcrafted by a human programmer in the crucial systematization step of the AI methodology. *And it is the syntactic details of these representations which do most of the work in an AI system.* In ignoring the importance of this fact, AI is engaging in a dance which Dennett has christened the "Dreyfus-Minsky Three Step" (Pylyshyn and Demopoulos, 1986, pp. 187-188). Each time someone suggests that a crucial nuance or background assumption or bit of common sense has not been adequately represented in a particular systematization (or this fact is discovered through some catastrophic failure of the system), the increasingly frustrated AI programmer responds, "Just tell me *exactly* what is missing, and I will add it to the system!" And round and round we go.

It is not my intention here to draw any deep philosophical conclusion from these criticisms. I certainly do not want to deny that we consciously manipulate mental representations for some purposes, nor do I want to claim that intelligent behavior cannot be modeled, or perhaps even reproduced, on a computer. What I do wish to argue, however, is that there is currently no reason to believe that the formal manipulation of symbolic representations of isolated pieces of the world will ever achieve the kind of coverage and generality required for unconstrained interaction with realistic environments. When the task is inherently abstract and well-defined to begin with, or the messy complexity of the real world is artificially restricted to some small number of possibilities, AI systems can do rather well. But how would the classical AI methodology even begin to approach a "problem domain" such as the following?

> Build me a robot that can ride a bicycle across town and back,
> go down to Motor Vehicles and obtain a California driver's li-
> cense, play six innings of baseball, cook a gourmet dinner, and
> finish up with a rendition of Stephen Foster's 'Old Susannah'
> played on the piano. Oh, and when you think you're finished,
> don't call me — have the robot come tell me in person. (Bierre,
> 1985, p. 60)

Challenges such as this, which emphasize the versatility of intelligent behavior over narrow expertise, continue to go completely unanswered in AI. To my mind, this state of affairs represents an empirical failure of the classical AI methodology, and the reasons for this failure seem to lie deep within the methodology itself. Psychologists have a name for individuals whose intelligence is forever limited to very narrow domains. They are called *idiot savants*, and their condition is considered pathological. Is this the sort of intelligent behavior to which we should aspire? "A brilliant chess move while the room is filling with smoke because the house is burning down does not show intelligence" (Anatol Holt, quoted in Winograd, 1987b, p. 16).

1.4 An Alternate View

Criticism by its very nature is a destructive act. If someone insists on emphasizing the shortcomings of a particular research program, then I believe they have a responsibility to propose a plausible alternative. In an attempt to seriously address the problems raised in the previous section, I wish to now propose just such an alternate view of intelligent behavior. This reorientation draws upon a number of converging themes from within AI itself, as well as psychology, biology, sociology, and philosophy. It consists of three nontraditional answers to the questions posed at the beginning of this chapter. Each of these answers builds upon the previous one. There are choices at each step, and in principle one could accept an earlier answer without accepting later ones. However, to my mind at least, they do seem to form a logical progression and, like the traditional answers, work much better as a package than in isolation.

1.4.1 Intelligence as Adaptive Behavior

What does it mean, to be intelligent? I think that AI's traditional emphasis on expert reasoning in highly specialized technical domains is an unacceptably narrow characterization. Rather, I would like to argue that it is *adaptive behavior*, the much broader ability to cope with the complex, dynamic, unpredictable world in which we live, that is, in fact, fundamental. Language and abstract reasoning are certainly among the attributes which make us most uniquely human. However, they arrived relatively late on the evolutionary scene. If such capabilities are essential for intelligent behavior, then how did our ancestors, or any other animal for that matter, manage for millions of years without them? The world is full of complex, ill-defined problems which must be solved on a regular basis simply in order to survive. Our higher cognitive functions are our own particular human elaborations of this more basic competence for effectively coping with the world. If AI is ever to understand the versatility of intelligent behavior, then it must tackle head-on the problem of unconstrained interaction with realistic environments. Only then can we be certain that we are not simplifying away the most fundamental problems faced by an intelligent agent (Brooks, 1987).

The question of what constitutes intelligent behavior is currently undergoing something of a revolution within psychology itself. A growing number of psychologists are arguing that the traditional focus on academic skills alone ignores much of the human intellect (Sternberg, 1985; Gardner, 1983). In its place, a diverse collection of capacities is being explored. There is an especially strong emphasis on so-called "practical intelligence," that collection of skills brought to bear on the sort of problems encountered in one's daily life (Sternberg and Wagner, 1986). Sternberg, for example, has redefined intelligence as purposive adaptation to real world contexts (1985).

In choosing the term "adaptive behavior" to characterize this broader view of intelligence, I have in mind the evolutionary sense of the word, in which a trait is adaptive if it contributes to an animal's overall survival. What I am trying to emphasize is the way in which the behavior of an intelligent agent engaged in ongoing interaction with its environment is continuously adjusted to the changing internal and external circumstances of that interaction in such a way as to achieve the agent's objectives. Strictly speaking, "adaptive behavior" means behavior which is adjusted to environmental conditions.

Unfortunately, "adaptive" often also carries the connotation that some kind of long-term structural change (i.e. learning) is involved. For example, an adaptive production system is one which changes its rules with experience in order to improve its performance. Learning is obviously a terribly important feature of intelligent behavior. However, just as evolution is the process by which behavior becomes adaptive in the first place, learning is the process by which behavior remains adaptive throughout an agent's life in the face of a nonstationary environment. Neither of these processes are involved in the actual generation of a particular behavior at a particular point in time. When a doctor recommending treatment for a bacterial infection notices that his patient is choking and performs the Heimlich maneuver, that is adaptive behavior in the sense that I am using the term. Because of this experience, that doctor may never again discuss alternative treatments while his patients are eating, but that is an entirely different matter.

1.4.2   Adaptive Behavior as Structural Congruence

What are the mechanisms which underlie intelligent behavior? In looking to the nature of deliberative reasoning for an answer to this question, I think that AI has things exactly backwards. There is no doubt that we make and consciously manipulate mental representations for some purposes. But that does not necessarily imply that all, or even most, of our intelligent behavior derives from such manipulation. Consider the following story.

> Thomas Gladwin (1964) has written a brilliant article contrast-
> ing the method by which Trukese navigate the open sea, with
> that by which Europeans navigate. He points out that the Eu-
> ropean navigator begins with a plan — a course — which he has
> charted according to certain universal principles, and he carries
> out his voyage by relating his every move to that plan. His ef-
> fort throughout his voyage is directed to remaining "on course."
> If unexpected events occur, he must first alter the plan, then
> respond accordingly. The Trukese navigator begins with an ob-
> jective rather than a plan. He sets off toward the objective and
> responds to conditions as they arise in an *ad hoc* fashion. He
> utilizes information provided by the wind, the waves, the tide
> and current, the fauna, the stars, the clouds, the sound of the
> water on the side of the boat, and he steers accordingly. His
> effort is directed to doing whatever is necessary to reach the ob-
> jective. If asked, he can point to his objective at any moment,
> but he cannot describe his course. (Berreman, 1966, p. 347)

Suchman, an anthropologist who studies man-machine interaction and
its implications for cognitive science, argues that "we all act like Trukese,
however much some of us may talk like Europeans" (Suchman, 1987, p.
ix). Her point is that however useful plans (and, by implication, other such
representations) are for describing our behavior, their actual role during
most activity itself is necessarily minimal. The reason for this is that action is fundamentally *situated*, by which she means contingent upon the
actual situation as it unfolds. There is no way that an *a priori* prescription
can possibly anticipate all of the contingencies which might arise during a
given interaction with the real world, and an *a posteriori* rationalization
always suppresses the very details which were crucial during the action
itself. Suchman views these representations as useful resources for com-
municating about intelligent behavior, rather than the actual mechanisms
underlying such behavior. The primacy of actually taking action in the
real world over the abstract descriptions we sometimes make of it has also
been emphasized by researchers in AI (Brooks, 1987; Agre and Chapman,
1987; Winograd and Flores, 1986), biology (Maturana and Varela, 1980),
sociology (Garfinkel, 1967; Heritage, 1984), and philosophy (Dreyfus and
Dreyfus, 1988; Heidegger, 1962).

But then what are the mechanisms which underlie intelligent behavior? How can we account for the appropriateness of an intelligent agent's actions, given its objectives and immediate situation, if not by appealing to internal representations of those objectives and situations? Strictly speaking, all that is required for adaptive behavior is a *structural congruence* between the dynamics of an intelligent agent's internal mechanisms and the dynamics of its external environment. For example, if an animal's nervous system is organized in such a way that the animal escapes from attacking predators, searches out and consumes food when necessary, etc., then its behavior will be adaptive in the sense that I have defined the term. There is no further requirement that an external observer also be able to distinguish internal structural configurations, or even complex functions of such configurations, which correspond to representations of the animal's environment.

Of course, how the dynamics of an animal's internal mechanisms comes to have the appropriate structure in the first place is also an important, but entirely separate, question. The answer to this question must ultimately be an historical one. A biological system has the particular structure that it does because of the particular history of structural changes it has undergone (as a result of both its internal dynamics and external environmental perturbations), as well as those of its evolutionary ancestors.

This notion of structural congruence is derived from Maturana and Varela's biological theory of cognition (Maturana and Varela, 1987; Maturana and Varela, 1980; Varela, 1979). Their concept of *structural coupling* is especially relevant to the present discussion: "As long as a unity does not enter into a destructive interaction with its environment, we as observers will necessarily see between the structure of the environment and that of the unity a compatibility or congruence. As long as this compatibility exists, environment and unity act as mutual sources of perturbation, triggering changes of state. We have called this ongoing process 'structural coupling'" (Maturana and Varela, 1987, p. 99). Structural congruence is also related to Agre's account of *situated activity*, which emphasizes the way in which an intelligent agent's activity derives from the pattern of interaction between its internal machinery and the world (Agre, 1988). Shöner and Kelso's notion of dynamic patterns is also relevant here (Schöner and Kelso, 1988), as is Brooks' approach to the design of autonomous robot control systems (Brooks, 1986). The theme common to all of this work is that the appropriate patterns of behavior emerge from the dynamic interaction between an intelligent agent and its environment. The ability of its internal control mechanisms to somehow mirror the structure of its external environment is irrelevant.

1.4.3 Computational Neuroethology

How can intelligent behavior be simulated or reproduced on a computer, or any other artificial device for that matter? The alternative view of intelligent behavior which has been advocated above raises two significant methodological problems. First, how can the day to day practice of AI proceed under this new view? The classical AI methodology has not been at all successful at exploring the versatility of intelligent behavior. But if we reject the classical methodology, we lose the very simplifications that make AI research possible. When even the most mundane contingency arises in our everyday interactions with the real world, we may draw upon a diverse collection of cognitive skills and a lifetime's worth of accumulated knowledge to cope with it. But human beings are simply too complex to model whole, and next to nothing is known about the mechanisms underlying our adaptive behavior.

Fortunately, far simpler animals than human beings exhibit adaptive behavior. While such animals cannot play chess or prove theorems, they are capable of flexibly adapting their limited behavioral repertoire to a complex, everchanging world in ways that no current AI system can match. Adaptive behavior is, in some sense, the biological condition: a biological system remains alive only so long as the structural changes it undergoes as a result of its internal dynamics and environmental perturbations do not interrupt the network of processes which keep it alive (Maturana and Varela, 1987). Though this is perhaps a humbling thought in light of the original aspirations of AI, a robot with "only" the versatility of an insect would be an impressive achievement indeed.

It is a striking testament to human conceit how little effort in AI has been expended on modeling the behavior of simpler animals. While some of our higher cognitive functions appear to be unique among the animal world, there is no reason to believe that they are completely discontinuous with the capabilities of simpler animals. After all, human beings did evolve from simpler animals in the first place. Most scientific and technological endeavors seek to understand and construct simpler systems before tackling the most complex ones. However, under the classical methodology, the trend has been the exact opposite in AI (Brooks, 1987; Hood, 1986).

The second methodological problem raised by the alternative view of intelligent behavior presented above is how to design internal control mechanisms whose dynamics exhibit the required structural congruence with those of a given environment. One of the advantages of the representation hypothesis is that, due to the way in which the structure of the environment is directly mirrored in corresponding structures of the internal control mechanism, this design process is a relatively straightforward task. Of course, this direct encoding was also the source of the inflexibility and brittleness of the resulting systems, because the structure of the real world is always more complex than can be explicitly represented. But then how should we go about designing the required control mechanisms?

I think that the best way to address this problem is to turn to the only working examples of such mechanisms that we know of, namely the nervous systems of natural animals. Over the course of millions of years of evolution, these neural mechanisms have evolved precisely the proper dynamics required to support the adaptive behavior of the animals in which they are embedded. This strategy should certainly not be taken to imply that the necessary dynamics cannot be achieved by other means, only that nervous system represent at least one solution and are therefore worthy of study.

Historically, AI has ignored neuroscience as largely irrelevant to its goals (Reeke and Edelman, 1988). This strategy has been justified by a kind of autonomy thesis, shared with psychology, which holds that mental phenomena can be explained without appeal to the brain (Churchland, 1986; Pylyshyn, 1984). In this view, loosely speaking, the mind is independent of the so-called "wetware" of the brain in much the same sense that software is independent of the hardware on which it runs. Recently, however, this view has been changing. In fact, there is currently a great deal of enthusiasm for brain-style models of computation and their application to cognitive processes (Churchland and Sejnowski, 1988).

What I am proposing, then, is modeling the neural mechanisms underlying the ability of simpler natural animals to effectively cope with the environments in which they are embedded. Rather than trying to decompose human cognition into isolated modules of expertise and then attempt to reassemble the pieces, I want to understand the adaptive behavior of simpler whole animals first. This approach is incremental. The insights gained from modeling a simpler animal can then be applied to modeling a slightly more complex one. This methodology is also intended to be complementary to the classical AI paradigm. Only by studying both those aspects of intelligence which are uniquely human and those more fundamental abilities which are shared with many other animals can we hope to achieve a deep understanding of intelligent behavior in general.

The study of the behavior of animals in their natural environments, engaged in the everyday business of their existence (e.g. feeding, fighting, fleeing, and reproduction), is called *Ethology* (Lorenz, 1981). The study of the neuronal mechanisms underlying this natural behavior is called *Neuroethology* (Camhi, 1984). Extending this terminology, I will therefore call the computer modeling of the neural control of behavior in simpler whole animals *Computational Neuroethology*. Lest anyone be concerned that such animals are too simple to be interesting, it should be pointed out that all current evidence suggests that there is nothing simple about either the behavior or the neural mechanisms of so-called simpler animals (Altman, 1989; Selverston, 1988).

The working assumptions of computational neuroethology can be summarized as follows: (1) the ability to flexibly cope with the real world is a defining characteristic of intelligent behavior, and more fundamental than conscious deliberation; (2) adaptive behavior derives from a structural congruency between the dynamics of an intelligent agent's internal mechanisms and the dynamics of its external environment; (3) modeling the neural control of behavior in simpler whole animals will provide insights into the nature of the dynamics required for adaptive behavior, and eventually lead to an understanding of the successive elaborations of these mechanisms which are observed in higher animals.

Over a decade ago, Dennett (1978b) argued for just such a reorientation of AI away from the modeling of "sub-subsystems with artificially walled-off boundaries" and toward the modeling of simple "whole cognitive creatures." While he originally suggested the construction of completely imaginary creatures (e.g. "Martian three-wheeled iguanas"), he now argues that a closer connection to simpler natural animals may be far more productive:

> Several years ago, in "Why Not the Whole Iguana?", I suggested that people in AI could make better progress by switching from the modeling of human microcompetences (playing chess, answering questions about baseball, writing nursery stories, etc.) to the whole competences of much simpler animals. At the time I suggested it might be wise for people in AI just to invent

imaginary simple creatures and solve the whole-mind problem
for them. I am now tempted to think that truth is apt to be
both more fruitful, and, surprisingly, more tractable, than fic-
tion. I suspect that if some of the bee and spider people were to
join forces with some of the AI people, it would be a mutually
enriching partnership. (Dennett, 1987, p. 257)

1.5   An Artificial Insect

The methodology sketched above immediately raises a great many questions. Which simpler animals should be modeled? At what level of detail?
How does one go about designing a nervous system for controlling the behavior of an entire animal? Is enough known about the neural mechanisms
of behavior in simpler animals to proceed? If so, what sort of neural model
is required to capture these neural mechanisms? How are such neural controllers to be designed and analyzed? What sort of simulation tools are
required to test and debug these controllers? What are appropriate bench-
marks for assessing their success or failure? Most of these questions can only
be answered by empirical investigation, by actually attempting to create a
simulated animal and seeing what happens. Like the classical methodology,
computational neuroethology must ultimately be judged by whether or not
it produces models which are successful in illuminating the mechanisms of
intelligent behavior.

The remainder of this book describes just such an experiment in computational neuroethology. An artificial insect is developed, and it is embedded
in a simulated environment which poses problems similar to some of those
encountered by natural insects. This artificial insect is capable of exhibiting
some of the most basic behaviors required for long-term survival in such an
environment, including locomotion, wandering, recoil, edge-following, and
feeding. In addition, it is capable of switching appropriately between its
various behaviors as its internal and external conditions change. All of the
insect's behavior is generated by an artificial nervous system, whose design
is based in part upon specific neural circuits drawn from several natural
animals.

This artificial insect is intended to be an initial exploration into computational neuroethology. As such, its primary goal is to examine the feasibility of the approach outlined above, and to explore some initial models.
Nevertheless, the artificial insect has proven to be a surprisingly fruitful

endeavor. By disallowing the explicit manipulation of internal representations and refusing to abstract away the problem of adaptively coping with an actual environment, the design of its nervous system has had to face head-on a number of difficult issues. Happily, attention to biological detail has lead to a number of striking and unexpected similarities between neural and behavioral characteristics of the artificial insect and those of natural animals. The artificial insect has also allowed some fundamental issues to be discussed in a concrete way, such as a deeper exploration of the role played by internal representations in explaining the behavior of an intelligent agent, and how goal-oriented behavior can be integrated with reactive responses without requiring explicit internal representations. I will return to these issues in the final chapter.

Chapter 2

Biological Background

2.1 Introduction

The majority of this book is concerned with the design of an artificial nervous system for controlling the behavior of a simulated insect. The design of this insect draws upon a variety of work on the neurobiological basis of animal behavior. Because much of this literature has been ignored as largely irrelevant to the goals of AI, this chapter presents the background material necessary for understanding the approach taken in this book. The next section provides a brief introduction to some of the important principles of animal behavior. Then an overview of the basic concepts of neurobiology is presented.

2.2 Animal Behavior

What are the common behavioral principles exhibited by animals engaged in the everyday business of their existence? Broadly speaking, animal behavior can be divided into a number of major classes. Perhaps the simplest form of animal behavior is a *reflex*, in which some fast, stereotyped response is triggered by a particular class of environmental stimuli. The defining characteristic of a reflex is that the intensity and duration of the response is entirely governed by the intensity and duration of the stimulus (Carew, 1985). Reflexes allow an animal to quickly adjust its behavior to sudden environmental changes. Reflexes are commonly employed for such things as postural control, withdrawal from painful stimuli, and the adaptation of gait to uneven terrain.

Taxes or orientation responses are another simple class of behavior (Camhi, 1984). These behaviors involve the orientation of an animal toward or away from some environmental agent, such as light, gravity, or chemical signals. For example, female crickets exhibit positive phonotaxis during courtship, that is they orient to the calling song of a male (Murphey and Zaretsky, 1972).

Fixed-action patterns are a somewhat more complex form of behavior (Lorenz, 1981). A fixed-action pattern is an extended, largely stereotyped response to a sensory stimulus. The triggering stimulus for a fixed-action pattern is generally more complex and specific than for reflexes. The response itself usually involves a complex temporal sequence of component acts. While such a pattern may be triggered by the occurrence of a specific sensory stimulus, its intensity and duration is not particularly stimulus-governed. In fact, once a fixed-action pattern has been triggered, it will usually run to completion even if the triggering stimulus is removed. An example of a fixed-action pattern is an escape response, in which some distinguishing characteristic of an imminent predator attack triggers a sequence of evasive maneuvers on the part of the prey (e.g. cockroaches escaping from toads; Ritzmann, 1984). The fixed-action patterns of individual animals can also be interrelated in intricate ways, as is demonstrated by the elaborate courtship rituals between the male and female members of many animal species (e.g. guppies; Baerends *et al.*, 1955).

Despite the ubiquity of such responses as reflexes, taxes and fixed-action patterns, animal behavior is by no means solely reactive. Factors internal to an animal can also play an important role in the initiation, maintenance, or modulation of a given behavior. The sign or intensity of reflexes, for example, can change depending upon internal factors. The threshold for triggering most fixed-action patterns similarly varies with internal state.

Behaviors which show no simple or rigid dependence on external stimuli, but are instead governed primarily by the internal state of the animal, are known as *motivated behaviors*. In these behaviors, an animal's propensity to exhibit a given behavior such as feeding depends not only upon the presence of the appropriate environmental stimuli (i.e. food), but also upon internal *motivational* variables (i.e. hunger). Motivated behaviors are typically characterized by (1) grouping and sequencing of component behavior in time, (2) goal-directedness: the sequence of component behaviors generated can only be understood by reference to some goal, (3) spontaneity: the behavior can occur in the complete absence of any eliciting stimuli, (4) changes in responsiveness: the modulatory effect of the motivational state varies depending upon its level of arousal or satiation, (5) persistence: the behavior can greatly outlast any initiating stimulus, and (6) associative learning (Kupfermann, 1974).

Any individual animal consists of a large collection of reflexes, taxes, and fixed-action patterns, many aspects of which are under at least some motivational control. As an animal confronts its environment with this diverse behavioral repertoire, it must properly coordinate its many possible actions into coherent behavior directed toward its long-term survival. Toward this end, the behavioral repertoire of a natural animal typically exhibits a certain organization. Some behaviors normally take precedence over others. Some behaviors are mutually exclusionary (i.e. any behaviors which utilize the same motor apparatus for incompatible actions). Switches between different behaviors depend both upon environmental conditions and internal state. These relationships are often described as rigid and strictly hierarchical, with cleanly delineated behaviors and simple all or nothing switching between them. In reality, the relationships may be nonhierarchical, the organization can change depending upon the behavioral context, and behaviors can partially overlap so that discrete switches between them are sometimes difficult to identify.

Though the number and variety of behavior clearly varies from species to species, all of the principles described above are exhibited in one form or another by all natural animals. This basic organization of behavior supports the ability of natural animals to flexibly cope with real world environments. In addition to this propensity for adaptive behavior, however, natural animals also exhibit various forms of *plasticity*. Aspects of their future behavior can be modified as a result of their past history of interactions with the environment. The time scale of these modifications may range from seconds to years.

Several simple forms of plasticity have been identified in natural animals (Kandel, 1976). In *habituation*, the magnitude of response to a given stimulus decreases with repeated exposure to the stimulus. For example, while a loud clap may initially produce a startle response in an animal, subsequent claps will produce a progressively weaker response. In some cases, the startle response may disappear altogether. *Dishabituation* is the sudden restoration of an habituated response following a particularly strong or noxious stimulus to the habituated sensory apparatus. An extremely loud clap, for example, might restore the habituated startle response. *Sensitization* involves an enhancement of a response following the presentation of a particularly strong or noxious stimulus. For example, a strong pinch might increase the sensitivity of the startle response to sound. These simple forms of plasticity allow an animal to adjust its responsiveness to its environment. The changes involved may last from minutes to weeks.

None of the above forms of plasticity depend upon a pairing of the strong stimulus with the weaker one. In *associative learning*, on the other hand, pairing between two stimuli is crucial. In one form of associative learning, called *classical conditioning*, repeated pairing of an initially neutral stimulus with one which normally elicits some response will eventually lead to a situation in which the neutral stimulus alone triggers the response. A common example of classical conditioning is when dogs salivate at the sound of a bell if the bell has been paired with the appearance of food in the past. In another form of associative learning, called *instrumental conditioning*, an animal's behavior is reinforced by events in its environment. For example, a rat will learn to avoid a particular food if prior ingestion of that food was followed by sickness (Garcia *et al.*, 1974). These associational forms of plasticity allow an animal to take into account the causal relationships within its particular environment. However, it is important to realize that most animals cannot make arbitrary associations, but only those that are biologically relevant. For example, though a rat can easily learn to associate illness with a particular odor or taste, it by and large cannot learn to associate illness with auditory or visual stimuli.

Though there are several other forms of behavioral plasticity, only one more will be mentioned here. *Latent learning* is plasticity which does not involve particularly strong stimuli or obvious reward or punishment, as when an animal learns about its environment through exploration. For example, even ants can learn to run a maze simply by repeatedly being placed within it (Schneirla, 1953). By these and many other forms of behavioral plasticity, animals fine-tune the behavioral repertoire with which they are genetically endowed to the exigencies of the particular environment in which they find themselves.

This section has focused primarily on characterizing the behavior of simpler animals. This emphasis should not be misunderstood. Human beings are obviously not insects, and there are many aspects of human behavior of interest to AI which clearly cannot be directly addressed through a study of simpler animals. I maintain, however, that there are many more which can. In particular, I strongly believe that the behavior of simpler animals has all of the ingredients which artificial autonomous agents require in order to flexibly cope with the real world: it is goal-oriented, adaptive, opportunistic, plastic, and robust. While the specifics of any given animal behavior are unlikely to be of direct use to an engineered agent, the general principles most certainly are.

2.3 Neurobiology

Consider the following problem: You must design the control system for a device which can autonomously accomplish some open-ended task (such as "stay out of trouble" or "keep this area clean") in a complex, dynamic, unpredictable, and, in many ways, openly hostile environment. You have considerable general information about the structure of this environment, but cannot assume that this information is complete in any sense. Your system must therefore be capable of flexibly applying whatever behavioral repertoire you choose to give it to the actual situations it encounters. At the same time, it must be capable of modifying aspects of that repertoire to better fit the particular environment in which it finds itself.

This task is far easier than the one that evolution faces, because evolution cannot benefit from the knowledge of any conscious designer. The only information that it has about the environment is whether or not a given design succeeds in reproducing itself. On the other hand, because it has so little information to go on, its designs make the fewest possible assumptions, resulting in the most robust control systems in existence. Evolution's answer to this challenge is nervous systems.

No brief introduction can do justice to the complexity of a single neuron, let alone an entire nervous system. The focus of this section is therefore on developing only the most basic concepts and terminology required to understand the organization of nervous systems. More thorough treatments can be found in (Llinás, 1989; Kandel and Schwartz, 1985; Shepherd, 1988).

First and foremost, a neuron is a living cell, with all of the biochemical processes that this implies. However, like all cells, neurons are specialized for the particular functions that they perform. The primary function of nerve cells is to coordinate the diverse actions available to an animal into behavioral responses appropriate to the internal and external conditions of its body as a whole. Consequently, neurons are specialized for integrating information from a variety of sources and sending signals which can affect specific cells over long distances.

2.3.1 Morphology

Neurons come in a great variety of shapes, each specialized for a different functional role (Figure 2.1). However, several general morphological characteristics are common to most neurons (Figure 2.2). The *cell body* or *soma* contains the basic biochemical machinery necessary for cellular function. Extending from the cell body are one or more branching processes. These processes are generally divided into two classes. The *dendrites* integrate signals from other neurons, while the *axon* serves to carry signals to other cells. The axon grows out of the cell body at a place known as the *initial segment* or *axon hillock*. Axons can extend over very long distances, in some cases more than a meter. Near their end, they divide into fine branches which end in *presynaptic terminals*. These terminals form specialized junctions known as *synapses* with other nerve cells.

2.3.2 Resting Potential

Transient electrical signals are the primary mode of operation of nervous systems. Even at rest, a nerve cell is polarized: its inside is electrically negative with respect to its outside. This *resting potential* is the result of a number of competing processes which cause the movement of charged particles through the cell membrane and lead to small but significant differences in charge across the membrane. A variety of positively and negatively charged ions are present both within the cell and surrounding it. The most important ion species are potassium (K^+), sodium (Na^+), and chloride (Cl^-). The cell membrane, which is primarily a fatty or lipid bilayer, is generally impermeable to these ions. However, embedded in the membrane are specialized proteins, known as *channels*, which allow the passage of selected ions through the membrane. Of primary interest for the resting potential are the *passive* or *nongated* channels, which always allow the free flow of selected ions.

Two major forces act to move ions through these channels. A chemical force results from the tendency of ions to diffuse from areas of high concentration to areas of low concentration. For example, because nerve cells actively maintain a high concentration of K^+ within the cell and a low concentration outside, potassium ions would tend to flow out of the

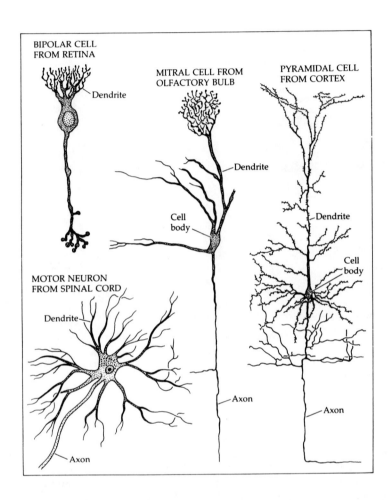

Figure 2.1: The diversity of nerve cell morphology. Four different types of vertebrate neurons are shown, each specialized for the particular function that they perform. (Figure 1 (p. 10), *From Neuron to Brain*, by S.W. Kuffler, J.G. Nichols, and A. R. Martin, Sinauer Associates, Sunderland, Massachusetts (1984).)

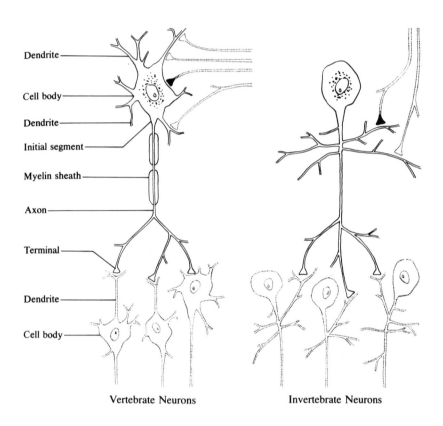

Dendrite

Cell body

Dendrite

Initial segment

Myelin sheath

Axon

Terminal

Dendrite

Cell body

Vertebrate Neurons   Invertebrate Neurons

Figure 2.2: General morphological characteristics of nerve cells. Typical vertebrate and invertebrate neurons are shown. The primary difference between vertebrate and invertebrate nerve cells are the location of the dendrites and the presence of a myelin insulating sheath which increases the signal transmission velocity in vertebrates. (From *Cellular Basis of Behavior*, by Eric Kandel. Copyright ©1976 by W.H. Freeman and Company. Reprinted with permission.)

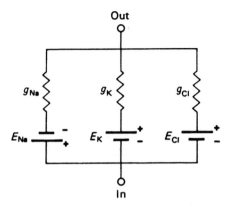

Figure 2.3: Equivalent circuit which represents the mechanisms responsible for the resting potential. The chemical and electrical forces acting on each ion species are represented as batteries. The passive channels are represented as conductances. (Reprinted by permission of the publisher from *Principles of Neural Science*, by E.R. Kandel and J.H. Schwartz, p. 62. Copyright ©1985 by Elsevier Science Publishing Co., Inc.)

cell through the appropriate channels. As ions move out of the cell under the influence of this chemical force, an opposite electrical force results from the tendency of ions to be attracted by regions whose net charge is of the opposite sign and repelled by regions whose net charge is of the same sign. Similar forces act on all of the ion species to which the membrane is permeable. The final resting potential of a nerve cell depends upon the dynamic equilibrium of these two forces for all ion species, and their relative permeabilities. This potential can be summarized by the electrical equivalent circuit shown in Figure 2.3. In this circuit, the various forces acting on each ion species are represented as batteries and the passive channels are represented as conductances.[1]

2.3.3   Passive Membrane Properties

In addition to batteries and conductances, the membrane of a nerve cell also exhibits capacitance. In general, capacitance results from the separation of charges by an insulating material. As mentioned above, except for the

---

[1] Conductance (denoted by G) describes the ease with which current can flow through a pathway. It is the inverse of resistance (G = 1/R), and has units of Siemens (1 S = $1\Omega^{-1}$).

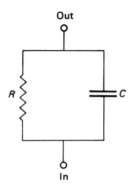

Figure 2.4: The electrical equivalent circuit for a passive patch of membrane is simply an RC. (Reprinted by permission of the publisher from *Principles of Neural Science*, by E.R. Kandel and J.H. Schwartz, p. 67. Copyright ©1985 by Elsevier Science Publishing Co., Inc.)

various channels embedded in it, the membrane is essentially an insulator. If we ignore the batteries by taking all voltage measurements relative to the resting potential, and lump all of the passive channels into a single conductance, then the passive properties of a small patch of membrane can be represented as an RC circuit (Figure 2.4).

The passive properties of the neuronal membrane have two important functional consequences: *temporal summation* and *spatial summation*. Temporal summation occurs because the RC slows the response of the membrane to a brief current injection. The effects of closely spaced current injections will tend to sum because the change in membrane potential resulting from one pulse will have insufficient time to decay before the next one begins. Temporal summation is characterized by the *time constant* (τ) of a patch of membrane, which is the time it takes the membrane potential of that patch to reach 63% of its final value. As in any RC circuit, τ is equal to the product of the membrane resistance and capacitance.

As discussed above, nerve cells have a great variety of complex shapes. The passive properties of each small patch of membrane can be described by an RC circuit. The passive properties of the entire cell can therefore be described by a complex network of such RC circuits. Spatial summation occurs because currents injected into the membrane spread throughout this network, decaying exponentially with distance. Therefore, the effects of currents injected into multiple places in the membrane will tend to sum if they are sufficiently closely spaced. Spatial summation is characterized by the *length constant* of the membrane, which, for a cylindrical axon, is the distance at which the change in membrane potential resulting from a given current injection has decayed to 37% of its original value. The combination of temporal and spatial summation has important functional consequences for the integrative capabilities of nerve cells. These purely passive properties, coupled with the intricate shapes of neurons, can result in selective responses to complex spatiotemporal patterns of inputs (Rall, 1977).

2.3.4 Active Membrane Properties

In addition to the passive properties resulting from the passive channels and capacitance of the membrane, a nerve cell also exhibits a variety of active properties. These result from another class of channels embedded in the membrane which are known as *active* or *gated* channels. Like passive channels, active channels also allow the flow of selected ions through the otherwise impermeable membrane. However, unlike passive channels, active channels may be either open or closed, depending upon such factors as the membrane potential or the presence of various chemicals. Critical characteristics of active channels include the ion species which they allow to pass through them, the rate with which they open or close, and the factors which control whether they are open or closed.

An important membrane property associated with active channels is the generation and conduction of *action potentials*. As discussed above, changes in potential due to the passive spread of current through the membrane decay exponentially with distance. Such signals therefore flow only a small distance (typically no more then a few millimeters) before they die out. In some neurons (called *nonspiking neurons*), this is sufficient for communication with other cells (Pearson, 1976b). However, many nerve cells need to transmit signals over longer distances. For this purpose, they make use of action potentials: brief, regenerative, positive excursions in membrane potential which are generally initiated in the axon hillock and travel down the axon to the presynaptic terminals (Figure 2.5).

In the Hodgkin-Huxley model (Hodgkin and Huxley, 1952), voltage-gated channels for K^+ and Na^+ are primarily responsible for the action potential. Voltage-gated Na^+ channels serve to *depolarize* the membrane (make it more positive than its resting potential) by allowing Na^+ to flow

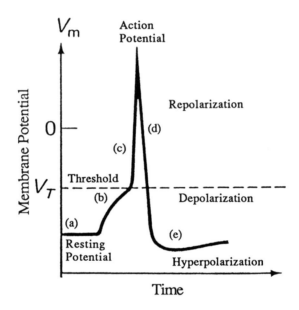

Figure 2.5: Changes in membrane potential during an action potential. Initially the cell is at its resting potential (a). When an external current is applied, the cell begins to depolarize (b). Eventually, the depolarization becomes explosive (c). Shortly after it has begun, this process is quickly reversed (d). Immediately after an action potential, the membrane potential actually falls somewhat below its resting level before it returns to normal (e). (Reprinted by permission of the publisher from *Principles of Neural Science*, by E.R. Kandel and J.H. Schwartz, p. 81. Copyright ©1985 by Elsevier Science Publishing Co., Inc.)

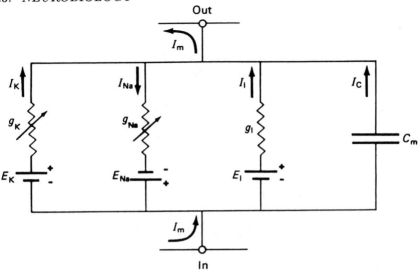

Figure 2.6: Electrical equivalent circuit for an active patch of membrane. The active K^+ and Na^+ channels which are responsible for the action potential are represented as variable conductances. (Reprinted by permission of the publisher from *Principles of Neural Science*, by E.R. Kandel and J.H. Schwartz, p. 78. Copyright ©1985 by Elsevier Science Publishing Co., Inc.)

into the nerve cell. These channels rapidly open for a short period of time when the cell is depolarized. Voltage-gated K^+ channels, on the other hand, serve to *hyperpolarize* the membrane (make it more negative than its resting potential) by allowing K^+ to flow out of the cell. These channels also open when the cell is depolarized, but more slowly than the voltage-gated sodium channels. The effects of these channels can be incorporated into the electrical equivalent circuit for a patch of membrane as variable conductances, whose values are both voltage and time dependent (Figure 2.6).

The sequence of events leading to an action potential begins with the nerve cell at its resting potential (Figure 2.5a). As it is depolarized, Na^+ channels begin to open, further depolarizing the cell (Figure 2.5b). When this inward sodium current exceeds the net outward current caused by the compensatory mechanisms responsible for the resting potential, this positive feedback process becomes explosive, causing the membrane potential to rapidly become very positive (Figure 2.5c).[2] After a short delay, the

---

[2]The membrane potential at which this explosive process occurs is generally referred

Na$^+$ channels begin to close. In addition, the depolarization causes the somewhat slower K$^+$ channels to begin to open. These two processes combine to rapidly send the membrane potential back toward its resting level (Figure 2.5d). In fact, for a brief period of time after the action potential, the membrane is actually slightly hyperpolarized due to the slow closing of the voltage-gated K$^+$ channels (Figure 2.5e). This process repeats itself throughout the axon. The currents responsible for an action potential in one patch of membrane depolarize an adjacent patch above threshold, causing an action potential to travel down the length of the axon.

After a short period of time, another action potential can be generated in the same patch of membrane. In general, the frequency of action potentials generated by a nerve cell is related to the magnitude of depolarizing current as shown in Figure 2.7. Below a certain level of current, no action potentials are generated. Just above this threshold, a train of action potentials are generated at some minimum firing frequency. The frequency of action potentials increases approximately linearly as the level of depolarizing current is increased, until saturation is reached at some maximum firing frequency.

In addition to the voltage-gated Na$^+$ and K$^+$ which are primarily responsible for the action potential, most nerve cells have an incredible variety of other active channels with various voltage, chemical and time dependencies (Llinás, 1988). The distribution of these many channel types across the membrane of a nerve cell is nonuniform. Their combination often results in responses which are considerably more complex than that shown in Figure 2.7. For example, they can lead to spontaneous, rhythmic activity in some nerve cells (Kandel, 1976; pp. 260-268).

2.3.5   The Synapse

Neurons communicate with each other at junctions known as *synapses* where the presynaptic terminal of one nerve cell comes into contact with the postsynaptic membrane of another one. There are two major classes of synapses: *electrical* and *chemical*. Electrical synapses occur when the presynaptic terminal of one cell is in electrical continuity with the postsynaptic cell, so that current can flow directly between them. These synapses are usually bidirectional: polarization in either cell affects the other. Electrical synapses tend to synchronize the firing of nerve cells.

---

to as the *threshold voltage*. However, due to the ionic basis of the underlying mechanisms, there is no unique voltage associated with the generation of an action potential.

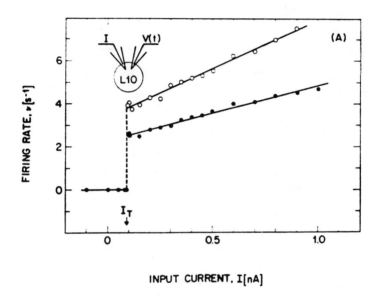

Figure 2.7: Relationship between depolarizing current and firing frequency in a cultured L10 nerve cell from the marine mollusc *Aplysia*. Solid circles describe the relationship at steady state, while open circles show the relationship shortly after the external current was applied. (Reproduced from the *Biophysical Journal*, 1990, Vol. 57, pp. 697-715, by copyright permission of the Biophysical Society.)

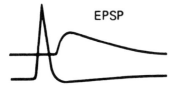 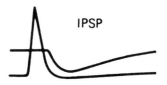

Figure 2.8: Typical postsynaptic potentials (PSPs) resulting from a single action potential in the presynaptic cell of a chemical synapse. (Left) An excitatory PSP or EPSP. (Right) An inhibitory PSP or IPSP. (Reprinted by permission of the publisher from *Principles of Neural Science*, by E.R. Kandel and J.H. Schwartz, p. 110. Copyright ©1985 by Elsevier Science Publishing Co., Inc.)

In contrast, chemical synapses are characterized by one-way transmission and much larger gaps between the presynaptic terminal and the postsynaptic membrane which make electrical continuity impossible. Instead, depolarization in the presynaptic terminal initiates a complex chain of biochemical events which culminates in the release of chemicals known as *neurotransmitters*. This depolarization is typically brought about by an action potential. However, in some nerve cells, transmitter is released in a more graded fashion solely as a result of the passive propagation of changes in membrane potential.

Once released, the neurotransmitters diffuse across the intervening space and activate chemically-gated channels in the postsynaptic cell, causing changes in its membrane potential. If the activated channels depolarize the cell, the synapse is termed *excitatory* and the potential change is called an *excitatory postsynaptic potential* (EPSP; Figure 2.8, Left). If the activated channels hyperpolarize the cell, the synapse is termed *inhibitory* and the change in membrane potential is called an *inhibitory postsynaptic potential* (IPSP; Figure 2.8, Right). By utilizing multiple neurotransmitters or multiple receptors, some synapses may have both excitatory and inhibitory components, each with different time courses (Getting and Dekin, 1985).

The polarization resulting from each PSP spreads passively through the postsynaptic neuron, temporally and spatially summing with other PSPs. If the resulting change in membrane potential is sufficient to depolarize some portion of active membrane to threshold, then it will fire an action potential. Synapses can occur on the dendrites of a nerve cell, on its cell body, on its axon, or on each other in very intricate configurations. Depending upon the placement of synapses on a neuron, its shape, the characteristics of each synapse, and its intrinsic properties, the response of a nerve cell to a given temporal and spatial pattern of input can be very complex.

2.3.6 Sensory and Motor Neurons

Though the majority of synapses occur between neurons, the activity of nerve cells does not exist in a vacuum. Two classes of nerve cells serve to connect the activity of neurons to the state of the body in which they are embedded: *sensory neurons* and *motor neurons*. Sensory neurons transduce physical properties of an animal's environment into electrical signals. The membranes of these nerve cells contain active channels whose configuration is affected by various physical properties, such as light intensity or force. As these channels open or close in the presence of the appropriate sensory stimulus, the membrane potential of a sensory neuron changes. The basic types of sensory receptors are chemoreceptors, mechanoreceptors, and photoreceptors.

Motor neurons, on the other hand, transform electrical signals into some form of action involving an animal's body. Action-producing organs are called *effectors*. The transformation from electrical activity to action is accomplished by synapses whose neurotransmitters trigger specific changes in the configuration of the associated effector organs. For example, motor neurons produce limb movement by releasing chemicals which cause specific muscles to contract or relax.

2.3.7 Neural Circuits

Even single neurons are capable of complex pattern recognition and processing tasks. However, most neural computation is accomplished by networks of nerve cells known as neural circuits. How are these circuits organized to support the behavioral principles discussed in the previous section? By a careful analysis of both the behavior and the underlying neural circuitry, this question is beginning to be answered in simpler animals.

Underlying reflexes in all animals, for example, are essentially direct connections between the sensory neurons which recognize the sensory stimulus and the motor neurons responsible for the response. Because these reflex circuits typically consist of short, fast pathways involving no more than one or two synapses, they are capable of only rudimentary sensory analysis and stereotyped motor responses. However, these reflex circuits may be affected by other circuits which interact with the neurons involved in the reflex (Watson and Burrows, 1985). Similarly, taxes and other orientation responses appear to be controlled by circuits which compare information from sensory receptors on each side of an animal's body (Rowel *et al.*, 1985).

All behaviors more complex than reflexes and taxes require the generation of temporally extended patterns of motor activity (e.g. fixed-action patterns). What is the neural basis of such patterns of behavior? How are the sequencing and timing of the individual components controlled? These questions have been most fully addressed in the context of rhythmic patterns of behavior, such as swimming or walking. The neural circuits underlying rhythmic behaviors are called *central pattern generators* or CPGs (Delcomyn, 1980).

CPGs can be divided into two general categories: those employing pacemaker cells and those employing network oscillators. Pacemaker cells are neurons which are capable of producing rhythmic bursts solely by virtue of their own intrinsic dynamics. Network oscillators, on the other hand, are networks of neurons which generate rhythmic patterns due to the synaptic interactions between their component neurons, none of which are capable of rhythmic activity in isolation. Often, central pattern generators involve networks of neurons with intrinsic bursting properties, so that the final pattern depends both upon the intrinsic dynamics of each cell as well as the interconnections between them (e.g. Selverston, 1988). In addition, the details and phasing of the basic pattern produced by a CPG can be so greatly affected by such external forces as sensory feedback, complex descending influences from higher "command" centers, and chemical modulation that many neurobiologists have begun to doubt the utility of the concept of a strictly *central* pattern generator (Pearson, 1985; Harris-Warrick and Johnson, 1989).

What are the neural mechanisms by which the internal state of an animal affects its behavior? There is no simple answer to this question. Many internal processes exist which can affect the function of particular neural circuits over time: (1) as already described, individual nerve cells have in-

trinsic cellular dynamics which influence their operation; (2) reverberating
pathways exist in which any activity in a circuit leads to increased activity within that same circuit via positive feedback loops; (3) the activity of
one nerve cell can dynamically alter the interactions between several others
via morphologically complex synaptic interactions; and (4) the activity of
a given neural circuit can be greatly influenced by a variety of chemical
means, such as hormones (Shepherd, 1988). Such capabilities allow the
possibility of dynamically rewiring any given anatomical circuit into many
functionally distinct networks (Getting and Dekin, 1985; Selverston, 1988).

Many situations require that a decision be made whether or not to
generate a specific behavior (e.g. some fixed-action pattern) in a given context. An early notion regarding the neural basis of such decisions was that
of a *command neuron* (Kupfermann and Weiss, 1978). In this view, sensory information converges on a single neuron which initiates the response
by activating the appropriate pattern generation circuitry only when the
proper sensory stimulus is present. A few examples of putative command
neurons have been found. However, though neurons whose activation can
elicit specific motor patterns certainly exist, the notion of a single neuron being uniquely responsible for a given behavior has proven to be an
oversimplification.

2.3.8 Nervous Systems

In order to accomplish the coordinated control of an entire animal body,
many individual neural circuits are organized into a single nervous system.
One of the most important problems which must be solved by a nervous
system as a whole is mediating between the potentially conflicting actions
of its constituent neural circuits. For example, when a cockroach is attacked
by a predator, it will either fly or run depending upon whether or not its
feet are in contact with the ground (Ritzmann, 1984). There must be some
neural mechanism for choosing between the circuitry responsible for each
of these two incompatible responses.

Neurobiologists have uncovered a variety of possible neural mechanisms
for behavioral choice (Kristan *et al.*, 1989). In some cases, the pattern
generator for one behavior can directly suppress the pattern generator of
another. In others, the pattern generator of one behavior does not directly
prevent the generation of another behavior, but instead blocks its expression
by denying it access to the required motor circuitry. Another possibility is
for the pattern generators for two behaviors to actually share circuitry in

such a way that the combined system is simply not capable of generating both patterns simultaneously. Finally, some cases may incorporate aspects of all three mechanisms. The general picture that is emerging is one in which behavioral choices are made in a distributed fashion by consensus among a variety of interacting neural pathways (Altman and Kien, 1989).

Nervous systems are specialized for the body in which they are embedded and the characteristics of the environmental niche with which they must cope. However, the nervous systems of diverse animals exhibit a number of important similarities. First, the basic problems faced by the nervous systems of all animals are quite similar. These include extracting the salient features of the environment, selecting behavior appropriate to the continuously changing internal and external conditions of the animal, utilizing the various effectors to accomplish specific behavioral goals, and modifying behavior as a function of experience. Second, the principles by which individual nerve cells operate are essentially the same in all nervous systems. Third, many of the same kinds of circuits (e.g. reflexes, central pattern generators, etc.) are found in all nervous systems, though they differ considerably in detail for different kinds of animals. Therefore, despite the fact that there has been an evolutionary trend toward increasingly elaborate and centralized organizations, much can and has been learned from the study of simpler nervous systems (Kandel, 1976).

2.3.9   Neural Plasticity

Generally speaking, neural plasticity refers to the ability of neural circuits to change their properties as a result of their recent history of activity. Such changes can occur on a variety of timescales, from milliseconds to years. These changes can also involve a variety of mechanisms, including electrical, biochemical, and even morphological changes. Chemical synapses in particular are the site of considerable plasticity. The strength of a synapse can be rapidly and reversibly affected by use, becoming either stronger (*facilitation*) or weaker (*depression*). In addition, an assortment of chemical *neuromodulators* can affect the characteristics of nerve cells. These various forms of neural plasticity may or may not be directly connected with identifiable behavioral plasticity (i.e. learning). Here we summarize several instances of neural plasticity which are associated with learning.

The cellular basis of several forms of behavioral plasticity have been extensively studied in some invertebrates, especially in the gill-withdrawal reflex of the marine mollusc *Aplysia*. In this reflex, tactile stimulation leads to a withdrawal of the animal's gill. Studies of the habituation of this response have shown that the decrement in the animal's response to a repetitive stimulus is associated with synaptic depression: the efficacy of specific synapses between sensory and motor neurons involved in the response decreases with repeated use (Kandel, 1985). This decrease is caused by prolonged inactivation of Ca^{2+} channels, which play a crucial role in the biochemical processes leading to the release of neurotransmitter.

Sensitization has also been studied in the gill-withdrawal reflex of *Aplysia* (Kandel, 1985). This response can be sensitized by delivering a noxious stimulus to the animal's tail. At the cellular level, sensitization involves synaptic facilitation: the efficacy of certain synapses involved in the response is increased by the sensitizing stimulus. The cellular basis of sensitization is somewhat more complex than that of habituation. Briefly, axons from sensory neurons triggered by the sensitizing stimulus excite facilatory interneurons which synapse near the synapses involved in the gill-withdrawal reflex. When the sensitizing stimulus occurs, these facilitory synapses release chemicals which, through a complex chain of biochemical events, increases the duration of action potentials in the sensitized synapses and otherwise acts to amplify the effect of a given presynaptic event. The net effect of these changes is that more neurotransmitter is released for a given presynaptic event than in the unsensitized synapse. Although habituation and sensitization involve cellular mechanisms which are by no means simple inverses, it is interesting to note that a sensitizing stimulus can reverse the effects of habituation in the gill-withdrawal reflex. In addition, it is known that long-term habituation and sensitization involve morphological changes to the synaptic membrane.

Finally, the cellular basis of classical conditioning has also been studied in the gill-withdrawal reflex of *Aplysia* (Kandel, 1985). The gill-withdrawal reflex may be triggered by stimulating either the animal's mantle or siphon. If stimulation of, say, the mantle, is repeatedly paired with the delivery of a noxious stimulus to the tail, then stimulation of the mantle alone will come to cause a more vigorous withdrawal response than stimulation of the siphon. The cellular basis of this association appears to be closely related to that involved in sensitization. It turns out that the presynaptic facilitation underlying sensitization is further enhanced by pairing with activity in the postsynaptic cell. In other words, the facilitation of a synapse by the mechanisms described above is greatly increased if the postsynaptic cell was recently active. Because it requires the co-ocurrence of two events

— activity in the facilatory interneuron and in the sensitized synapse — this activity-dependent presynaptic facilitation is much more selective than that involved in simple sensitization, and can therefore encode the association of events.

2.3.10   Neural Development

The organization of nervous systems is neither uniform nor random, but the result of specific developmental processes (Spitzer, 1982). Shortly after nerve cells appear in the developing organism, they begin to take on their unique morphological and functional characteristics. As they continue to grow and differentiate into their final forms, they must often migrate over considerable distances. In addition, developing nerve cells send out branching axons which eventually synapse on specific areas of particular cells or cell types. Thus, these developmental processes result in the construction of very specific patterns of nerve cells and neural circuits.

Two major mechanisms are responsible for neural development (and for development in general). First of all, many of the characteristics of the mature nervous system are determined by the genetic instructions encoded in the DNA of each cell. Secondly, a variety of factors can modulate the expression of this genetic information. Such factors include the functional activity of developing nerve cells, the exchange of chemical signals, and competition between them for nutrients. The relative contribution of each of these processes to neural development varies from species to species. Speaking very generally, the neural development of simpler invertebrates appears to be largely determined genetically. The neural development of higher vertebrates, on the other hand, appears to be governed to a much greater extent by the dynamics of cellular interactions. Part of the reason for this difference may simply be the fact that, because vertebrate brains have so many more nerve cells than invertebrates, a great many more cell divisions are required to generate them. This allows a greater opportunity for cellular interactions to occur before nerve cells become committed to their fates. Even in the case of simpler invertebrates, however, it is important to realize that the genome acts more as a regulator of a complex, interacting set of developmental processes than as a simple blueprint.

The processes underlying the development of nervous systems do not terminate at birth. Rather, they continue into early life and, to some extent, extend throughout most of the life of an animal. Indeed, many of the mechanisms responsible for the ability of nervous systems to change their structure as a function of their activity are essentially continuations of these processes. Such general plasticity is thought to underlie the specific mechanisms responsible for learning and memory (Shepherd, 1988).

Chapter 3

The Artificial Insect

3.1 Introduction

In order to explore the neural control of behavior in a simulated insect, a specific body and an environment for it to cope with must be chosen. In addition, a neural model to be used in constructing its nervous systems must be selected. These decisions are not arbitrary, but significantly impact the behavioral repertoire and the design of the nervous system of the resulting artificial insect. In this chapter, the physical models chosen for the body and the environment in which it is embedded are described in detail. A model neuron which captures some of the characteristics of nerve cells which appear to be essential for the neural control of behavior in natural animals is then presented. Finally, some details of the simulation and its user interface are discussed.

3.2 Physical Models

3.2.1 Body

Choosing a proper body design for the artificial insect is more important than it may first appear. The choice defines the kinds of interactions the organism can enter into with its environment. In addition, as we shall see in Chapter 5, the body can have important consequences for subtle aspects of the operation of the nervous system which controls it. Choosing too simple a body for the insect may severely limit the interest of the behaviors

45

it can exhibit. An organism whose body is a point has very little need for a
nervous system. With too sophisticated a body, on the other hand, we run
the risk of overwhelming our model with physical complexities and overly
difficult low-level sensorimotor control problems.

The body of the artificial insect is shown in Figure 3.1. Though this design is loosely based upon *Periplaneta americana*, the American Cockroach
(Bell and Adiyodi, 1981), it resembles the basic body plan of many insects.
The antennae contain both tactile and chemical sensors. The mouth can
open and close, and also contains tactile and chemical sensors. The two
antennae-like structures in the rear are known as cerci, and are currently
unused. The artificial insect is called *Periplaneta computatrix*, the Computer Cockroach.[1]

The artificial insect also has six legs, each with a foot that may be either
up or down. When its foot is up, a leg assumes a fixed length and any forces
it applies cause it to swing. When its foot is down, a leg stretches between
its foot and the body, and any forces it generates may result in movement
of the body. Despite the fact that the insect is only two-dimensional, it is
capable of "falling down." The insect becomes statically unstable whenever
its center of mass lies outside of the polygon formed by the feet which
are down. If this condition persists for longer than 40 msec, the insect is
considered to have fallen down and the legs are no longer allowed to move
the body.

In addition, the insect possesses a finite store of energy, and a simple
metabolism in which energy is consumed at a fixed rate. If its energy level
falls to zero, the insect is removed from the environment. Whenever the
insect's mouth closes over a patch of food, a fixed number of food units
is transferred from the patch to the insect. Repeated opening and closing
of the mouth (biting) can therefore be used to consume the food. As the
food is transferred from the patch to the insect, the patch's size and odor
strength decrease accordingly. In the present simulation, food patches are
nonrenewable resources. A more detailed description of the body model
may be found in Appendix A.

---

[1] This name was inspired by Arbib's model of visually guided behavior in frogs and
toads, *Rana computatrix* (Arbib, 1987). Arbib in turn acknowledges the influence of W.
Grey Walter's *Machina Speculatrix* (Walter, 1953).

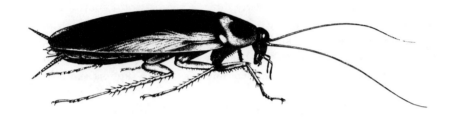

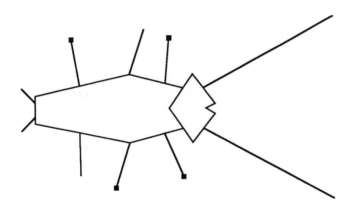

Figure 3.1: (Top) *Periplaneta americana*, the American Cockroach. (From *The Escape System of the Cockroach*, by J.M. Camhi, *Scientific American*, Vol. 243, No. 6, p. 162.) (Bottom) *Periplaneta computatrix*, the Computer Cockroach. Feet which are currently providing support to the body are denoted by black squares.

3.2.2   Environment

Given the discussion above, it should come as no surprise that the choice
of an environment in which to embed *P. computatrix* is as important as
the choice of a body for it. Together, the body and environment define the
kinds of behaviors that the insect can exhibit. Like the choice of a body,
the choice of too simple an environment will allow only a trivial behavioral
repertoire, while too complex an environment will be computationally expensive to simulate and pose overly difficult sensorimotor control problems
which are not of direct interest here. General-purpose Newtonian physics
simulation environments such as the World Modeling System (Hood and
Carbonell, 1982) have therefore been avoided. Instead, a special-purpose
physical simulation which is only complex enough to support the behaviors
of interest is employed.

In this simplified physics, the velocity of an object is directly proportional to the force applied to it and inversely proportional to its mass
($F \propto mv$). Rotational velocity is similarly related to torque and rotational inertia ($T \propto I\omega$). Space in the simulation is continuous, but time is
divided into discrete 20 millisecond intervals. In each fixed time step, the
simulator sums the forces acting upon each object and updates its velocity
and position accordingly.

The simulated environment can optionally be enclosed by walls formed
by the edges of the screen. When these walls are not present, the environment forms a torus. Rectangular "bricks" may also be present and arranged
in any desired pattern. Bricks and walls are the only objects with which
insects can physically interact. When an insect encounters a brick or wall, a
collision occurs. Again, the physics of collisions has been greatly simplified.
Walls and bricks are unmovable. When an insect contacts such an object,
it bounces back along the direction of motion of the point of contact by a
small, fixed amount.

In addition, the simulated environment may contain circular "patches."
For purposes of physical interaction, these patches can be thought of as
lying in a separate plane from insects, bricks, and walls. These patches
may thus be walked over without any possibility of collision. In the current
behaviors, these are primarily used to represent food. Such food also gives
off an odor whose strength is proportional to the number of food units
contained within the patch, which in turn is proportional to the area of the
patch. As these odors diffuse through the environment, their intensity falls
off as the inverse square of the distance from the center of the food patch.

Currently, bricks do not serve as impediments to the diffusion of odors.

3.3 Neural Model

The essential challenge of the artificial insect is to use ideas drawn from biology to design a nervous system capable of generating all of the behaviors necessary to the survival of *P. computatrix*. To this end, we require a neural model which strikes the proper balance between the complexity of biological nervous systems and the requirements and constraints of our simulation. In this section, a model neuron for use in *P. computatrix* is developed. This model is then used to construct a pacemaker neuron which will be employed in later controllers.

The model neuron employed in this book is intermediate in complexity between those typically employed in artificial neural networks and computational neuroscience. Like the formal neurons of artificial neural networks, it ignores the details of action potential generation and most of the complexities of synaptic and dendritic interactions. However, it draws some of the characteristics of its input-output relationship from the more realistic models. It is most similar to Hopfield's continuous, deterministic model, which includes the passive RC characteristics of the cell membrane (Hopfield, 1984) It differs from this model in its choice of input/output function, its inclusion of time-dependent properties, and the nonuniformity of its elements and their interconnections.

The model neuron is shown schematically in Figure 3.2. It represents the firing frequency of a cell as a nonlinear function of its input potential. Based upon the relationship between depolarizing current and firing frequency for nerve cells discussed in Section 2.3.4 (Figure 2.7), a saturating linear threshold function with an initial jump discontinuity has been used for this relationship (see inset). This input/output function is characterized by three parameters: the threshold voltage at which the neuron begins to fire, the minimum firing frequency, and the gain. The substitution of membrane potential for depolarizing current in this relationship is justified by the fact that the rapid voltage swings that underlie action potentials are being ignored. In that case, a similar relationship holds between steady-state voltage and firing frequency as holds between depolarizing current and firing frequency. The firing frequencies of all neurons are normalized to the range [0,1].

The passive RC properties of the cell membrane are also represented,

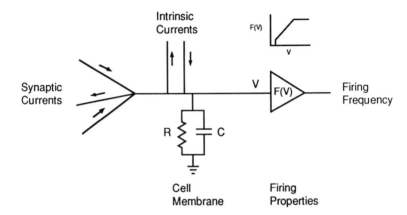

Figure 3.2: A schematic illustration of the model neuron.

capturing the ability of nerve cells to temporally sum their inputs. These
cells are interconnected by weighted synapses through which the firing of
one cell can cause currents to flow through the membrane of another cell. If
the output of a cell is thought of as voltage rather than firing frequency, then
these weights can be thought of as resistors (Hopfield, 1984). However, by
leaving intact the explicit connection between the output of a model neuron
and the firing frequency of a nerve cell, ithe weights become functions from
presynaptic firing frequency to postsynaptic current.

One of the most striking differences between real nerve cells and the formal neurons typically employed in artificial neural network research is their
rich intrinsic dynamics (Llinás, 1988). As discussed in the previous chapter,
nerve cells contain a wide variety of active conductances which endow them
with complex time-dependent responses to input and spontaneous activity.
Such properties appear to be crucial to the function of those neural circuits
which have been analyzed at the cellular level (Selverston, 1988). Without
modeling in detail the underlying active conductances, some of these intrinsic properties can still be captured by the addition of intrinsic currents
to the model (Figure 3.2). These intrinsic currents may simply be static
functions of membrane potential, or they may be described by their own
differential equations.

The membrane potential of each model neuron can be described by a differential equation of the following general form:

$$
\underbrace{C_N \frac{dV_N(t)}{dt}}_{Net\ Input\ Current} = \underbrace{\sum_{M \in pre(N)} S_{M,N} F_M(V_M(t))+}_{Synaptic\ Currents}
$$

$$
\underbrace{\sum_{L \in intrinsic(N)} INT_L(t, V_N(t))+}_{Intrinsic\ Currents}
$$

$$
\underbrace{EXT_N}_{External\ Current} - \underbrace{V_N(t)G_N}_{Leak\ Current}
$$

where C_N is the membrane capacitance of neuron N

$V_N(t)$ is the membrane potential of neuron N

$pre(N)$ is the set of neurons which form synapses on neuron N

$S_{M,N}$ is the strength of the connection from neuron M to neuron N

$F_M(V_M(t))$ is the firing frequency of neuron M

$intrinsic(N)$ is the set of intrinsic currents of neuron N

$INT_L(t, V_N(t))$ is the magnitude of intrinsic current L, which may be voltage and time dependent

EXT_N is the magnitude of external current injected into neuron N

G_N is the membrane conductance of neuron N

Networks of such neurons are represented by coupled sets of differential equations. These equations are integrated using Euler's method with a fixed time step of 5 milliseconds in the present simulation. Note that this neural timestep is a factor of four smaller than that used to update the physical model. The response of a typical model neuron containing no intrinsic currents to externally injected current is illustrated in Figure 3.3.

3.3.1 A Model Pacemaker

As an example of the use of intrinsic currents, consider the implementation of a pacemaker cell with this model neuron. Recall that a pacemaker cell is one which is capable of endogenously producing rhythmic bursting. Pacemakers are employed in a number of neural controllers to be presented in subsequent chapters. As described by Kandel (1976, pp. 260-268), a pacemaker cell exhibits the following characteristics: (1) when it is sufficiently hyperpolarized, it is silent, (2) when it is sufficiently depolarized, it fires

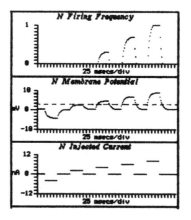

Figure 3.3: The response of a model neuron to the external injection of current. The bottom trace shows the magnitude of the injected current. Currents of -4, 2, 4, 6, and 8 nA were injected for 100 msec each at 100 msec intervals. The middle trace shows the change in membrane potential corresponding to each current injection. The threshold voltage is marked with a dotted line. The top trace shows the corresponding output firing frequency of the neuron. Note that the first two current injections were subthreshold, while the last current injection caused saturation. The model neuron had a membrane conductance of .5 μS, a membrane capacitance of 10 μF, a threshold of 5 mV, a gain of .1 mV^{-1}, and a minimum firing frequency of 0. No intrinsic currents were present.

continuously, (3) between these two extremes, it rhythmically produces a series of relatively fixed-duration bursts, and the length of the interval between bursts is a continuous function of the injected current, (4) a transient depolarization which causes the cell to fire between bursts can reset the bursting rhythm, and (5) a transient hyperpolarization which prematurely terminates a burst can also reset the bursting rhythm.

These characteristics can be reproduced with the above model neuron through the addition of two intrinsic currents. I_H (the High current) is a depolarizing current which tends to pull the membrane potential above threshold. I_L (the Low current) is a hyperpolarizing current which tends to pull the membrane potential below threshold. Rather than being governed by differential equations, for simplicity, these currents are manipulated according to the following rules: (1) I_H is triggered whenever the cell goes above threshold or I_L terminates, and it then remains active for a fixed length of time, and (2) I_L is triggered whenever I_H terminates, and it then remains active for a variable amount of time whose duration is a function of the steady state membrane potential. Only one of these two currents is active at any given time.

Figure 3.4 illustrates the variable burst frequency properties of the model pacemaker. As the level of injected current is varied, the interval between bursts similarly varies, being longer than normal for hyperpolarizing current and shorter than normal for depolarizing current. The variation of burst frequency with current injection is linear because the voltage dependence of I_L is currently linear. In addition, if sufficiently strong hyperpolarizing current is injected into the neuron, I_H will be unable to pull the membrane potential above threshold and the pacemaker will be silent. Likewise, if sufficiently strong depolarizing current is injected into the neuron, I_L will be unable to pull the membrane potential below threshold, and the pacemaker will burst continuously.

Figure 3.5 illustrates the reset properties of the model pacemaker. If a transient depolarization sufficient to fire the neuron occurs between bursts, a normal burst will begin and the bursting rhythm will have been reset. Likewise, if a transient hyperpolarization sufficient to pull the neuron below threshold occurs during a normal burst, a new burst will begin when the hyperpolarization terminates and I_H causes the membrane potential to recross threshold.

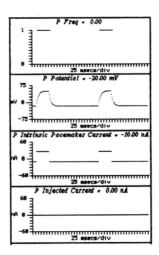

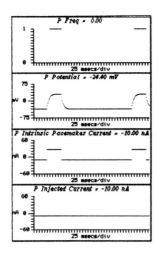

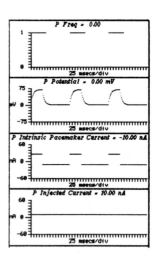

Figure 3.4: Variable interburst properties of a model pacemaker. In each display, the bottom trace panes show the magnitude of externally injected current. The traces above these show the value of the intrinsic pacemaker current $(I_L + I_H)$. At the top are shown traces of the membrane potential and output firing frequency. (Top) Even in the absence of any external current, the model pacemaker bursts rhythmically. (Lower Left) When hyperpolarizing current is injected, the model pacemaker bursts less frequently. (Lower Right) When depolarizing current is injected, the model pacemaker bursts more frequently.

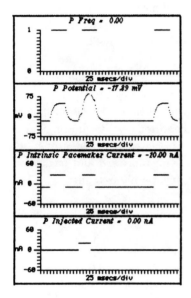
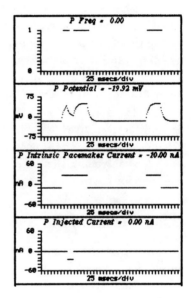

Figure 3.5: Reset properties of a model pacemaker. Arrangement of traces is the same as for the Figure 3.4. When a transient depolarizing current of sufficient magnitude occurs between bursts (left), or a transient hyperpolarizing current of sufficient magnitude occurs during a burst (right), the burst rhythm of the model pacemaker is reset.

3.3.2   Sensory and Motor Neurons

Sensory and motor neurons serve to connect the nervous system to the body in which it is embedded. A model sensory neuron has an intrinsic current whose magnitude is a function of the intensity of the physical stimulus to which its receptor is sensitive. Four classes of sensory neurons are utilized in this book: (1) chemoreceptors in the antennae and mouth are sensitive to the strength of the odor field at their location; (2) mechanoreceptors in the mouth are sensitive to the presence of a food patch directly beneath the mouth; (3) mechanoreceptors in the antennae are sensitive to the deflection of the tip of the antennae; (4) an energy sensor is sensitive to the amount of energy an insect possesses.

The state of a given effector is a function of the firing frequency of the model motor neuron which innervates it. Three classes of motor neurons are employed in this book: (1) the mouth opens whenever its motor neuron is sufficiently active; (2) a foot is down only so long as its motor neuron is sufficiently active; (3) each leg has three associated motor neurons, one each for controlling the force which with it swings forward and backward, and one for controlling the force with which it laterally extends.

3.3.3   Compound Synapses

In some cases, it is necessary to allow one model neuron to modify the effect that a second neuron has on a third. This can be accomplished via a compound synapse, in which one neuron synapses on the connection between two others. As briefly discussed in Section 2.3.5, morphologically complicated arrangements can occur between multiple presynaptic terminals, with complex functional consequences. The controllers described in this book make use of two classes of compound synapses: *gated* synapses and *modulated* synapses. A gated synapse is one which can be switched on or off, or inverted, by currents delivered from other synapses. A modulated synapse, on the other hand, is one whose gain can be continuously adjusted by other synaptic currents. These compound synapses are related to the sigma-pi (Rumelhart, Hinton, and McClelland, 1986) and product units (Durbin and Rumelhart, 1989) that have been employed in artificial neural networks. However, these models utilize symmetrical multiplicative interactions, while the interaction at a compound synapse is asymmetrical. Compound synapses are shown schematically in Figure 3.6.

Both classes of compound synapses involve modifications to the term

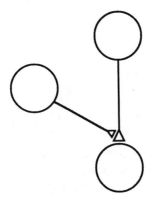

Figure 3.6: Schematic illustration of a compound synapse.

which represents standard synapses in the previous equation, namely $S_{M,N} F_M(V_M(t))$. For gated synapses, this synaptic current term takes the following form:

$$(U + I_G)I_S$$

where I_S represents the standard synaptic current term, U represents the ungated state of the synapse (either 1 for on or 0 for off), and I_G is the synaptic current from the gating synapse (which, like a standard synapse, is equal to the product of the firing frequency of the gating neuron and the strength of the gating connection). The essential idea here is that gating synaptic currents of the proper magnitude and sign can interact with U to turn on, turn off, or invert a gated connection.

In modulated synapses, on the other hand, this term takes the following form:

$$(1 + I_M)I_S \quad \text{if } I_M > 0$$
$$\frac{I_S}{1 + |I_M|} \quad \text{if } I_M < 0$$

where I_S represents the standard synaptic current term and I_M is the synaptic current from the modulatory synapse (which, like a standard synapse, is equal to the product of the firing frequency of the modulatory neuron and the strength of the modulatory connection). The essential idea here is that a modulatory synapse which is excitatory can increase the gain of the modulated synapse by an amount proportional to the modulatory synaptic current, whereas a modulatory synapse which is inhibitory can decrease the gain of the modulated synapse in a similar manner.

3.3.4   Related Work

There has been a great deal of work on the computer simulation of neural networks. Very broadly speaking, this work can be divided into three areas: computational neuroscience, artificial neural networks, and connectionism. While there is a great degree of overlap between these three endeavors, their underlying motivations are sufficiently different that it is worthwhile distinguishing them. Computational neuroscience (Sejnowski et al., 1988; Koch and Segev, 1989) is primarily concerned with the use of computer simulation to gain functional insight into biological nervous systems, and usually maintains a close tie to experimental data. In contrast, interest in artificial neural networks (Pao, 1989; DARPA, 1988) has centered on characterizing the computational properties of neural networks and applying them to a variety of practical problems. Finally, connectionism (Rumelhart and McClelland, 1986; McClelland and Rumelhart, 1986) is largely concerned with the use of neural networks as parallel distributed models of cognitive processes. All of these efforts have employed a variety of neural models. How do the neural networks developed in this book compare to these other models?

Work in computational neuroscience often utilizes very realistic simulations which are based upon mathematical models of the biophysical processes underlying the operation of nerve cells. Realistic models may be extremely accurate, or they may involve certain simplifications. Realistic models are distinguished from the more abstract models described below by the extent to which their simplifications and parameter values are tied to experimental data. Realistic models of single cells have been utilized to study such issues as the functional consequences of passive dendritic trees (e.g. Koch et al., 1983), the contribution of various active conductances to the response properties of nerve cells (e.g. Borg-Graham, 1988) and the investigation of synaptic plasticity (e.g. Byrne and Gingrich, 1989). Realistic models of small neural circuits have been particularly useful in clarifying some of the principles by which central pattern generators operate (e.g. Getting, 1989; Hartline, 1979). Finally, realistic models of small brain slices have examined the neural basis of their oscillatory dynamics (e.g. Wilson and Bower, 1989; Traub et al., 1989).

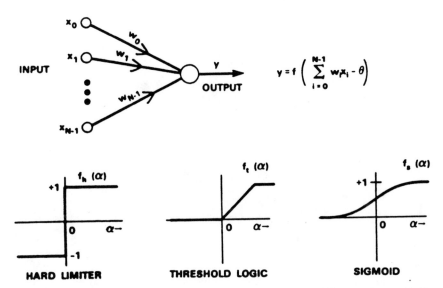

$$y = f\left(\sum_{i=0}^{N-1} w_i x_i - \theta\right)$$

Figure 3.7: Basic structure of a single formal neuron. The output activity is a nonlinear function of the weighted linear sum of the inputs. Three typical nonlinear activation functions are shown. (From *An Introduction to Computing with Neural Nets*, by R.P. Lippman, *IEEE ASSP Magazine*, Vol. 4, No. 2. ©1987 by IEEE.)

Some work in computational neuroscience, and nearly all work in artificial neural networks and connectionism, makes use of a so-called *formal neuron*, which represents a significant abstraction of the input/output behavior of nerve cells. This neural model can be traced to the binary neurons of McCulloch and Pitts, in which the output was one if the sum of the inputs was above a threshold and zero otherwise (McCullough and Pitts, 1943). In the most common modern form of these models, the output of a formal neuron (which is generally called its *activity*) is a simple nonlinear function of the weighted linear sum of its inputs (Figure 3.7). Three typical nonlinear input/output relationships are also shown in Figure 3.7. Formal neurons ignore a great many biological details. In essence, they reduce the complex dynamics of real nerve cells to simple time-indepedent functions, though some neural models do allow for simple time-dependencies (e.g. Hopfield, 1984; Grossberg, 1988). Despite these extreme simplifications, networks of these formal neurons appear to have many interesting computational properties.

Output Patterns

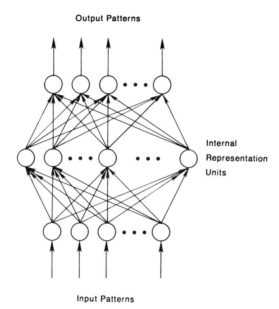

Internal
Representation
Units

Input Patterns

Figure 3.8: Architecture of a typical feedforward network. (Reprinted by permission of the publisher from *Learning Internal Representations by Error Propagation*, by D.E. Rumelhart, G.E. Hinton, and R.J. Williams, in *Parallel Distributed Processing*, Volume 1, edited by D.E. Rumelhart and J.L. McClelland. ©1986 by The Massachusetts Institute of Technology.)

Collections of formal neurons can be interconnected in a variety of ways. Perhaps the most well-known artificial neural network architecture is the multilayer, feedforward network. In the most general form of this architecture, formal neurons are arranged into one or more layers in which every element of a given layer connects to every element of the next higher layer in a feedforward fashion (Figure 3.8). Such architectures are particularly useful for pattern transformation tasks. An input pattern is presented to the bottom layer by appropriately setting the activities of the corresponding input units. These activities are then propagated forward by calculating the output activity of successive layers until an output pattern has been computed. Perhaps the most famous application of this architecture is NETtalk, which transformed a stream of English text into the phonetic sequence necessary to speak it (Sejnowski and Rosenberg, 1987).

Another influential artificial neural network architecture was developed by Hopfield (1982, 1984). The focus of this work was on content-addressable memory: the storage of a number of patterns, each of which can then be retrieved by the presentation of only a fragment of the original. Hopfield showed how multiple patterns could be stored as attractors in a fully connected network of formal neurons, and that the network would always converge to the stored pattern most closely matching a given input pattern. He also showed that the capacity of such a memory was approximately 15% of the number of formal neurons. In addition to associative memory, such networks have been used for solving optimization problems (Hopfield and Tank, 1985).

The model neuron utilized in this book owes much to the formal neurons that have been employed in artificial neural network research. Like them, it ignores the details of action potential generation and conduction, the passive spread of current through dendritic trees, and most of the complexities underlying synaptic transmission. However, there are important differences as well. The architectures utilized in artificial neural networks tend to be fairly homogeneous collections of formal neurons interconnected in some uniform manner (e.g. feedforward or fully interconnected). In contrast, individual nerve cells have often unique response properties (derived from the type and distribution of their channels, their morphology, and the placement of synapses on them) (Llinás, 1988). In addition, diverse collections of nerve cells are interconnected in very specific, highly nonuniform ways to form the neural circuits which constitute nervous systems. There is considerable evidence that both individual cellular properties and specific network connectivity are crucial to the ways in which neural circuits function (Selverston, 1988; Getting and Dekin, 1985; Bullock, 1976). Like nervous systems, the networks described in this book tend to be very heterogeneous: each model neuron can be endowed with distinctive intrinsic properties, and their patterns of interconnection are far from uniform. In order to emphasize both the uniqueness of the intrinsic properties of individual model neurons and the nonuniformity of their interconnection, this approach is termed *heterogeneous neural networks*.

Learning is a particularly important component of most work involving networks of formal neurons. Because the network architectures are so homogeneous, they must somehow be configured to perform any specific task. Typically, a network begins with a random assignment of weights to the connections between its formal neurons. A learning procedure is then used to train the network to generate the appropriate responses. Though many other techniques are currently being explored (Hinton, 1987), perhaps the most popular learning algorithm is backpropagation (Rumelhart, Hinton, and Williams, 1986). In this algorithm, the difference between the output produced by a feedforward network and the desired output is used to adjust the connection weights. It can be shown that this procedure approximates a gradient descent search of the error measure in weight space. While convergence to the required weights is not guaranteed with this procedure, it is relatively common in practice.

The plasticity of nervous systems is obviously crucial to their ability to rapidly adapt to new situations. However, I think that the importance of learning has been overemphasized in neural network research, to the detriment of architecture. In contrast to most artificial neural networks, nervous systems begin with a great deal of structure. This structure is the result of developmental processes, which have in turn been shaped by hundreds of millions of years of evolution. Learning is best viewed as a means by which these evolutionarily good designs are fine-tuned to the exigencies of particular environments, rather than as a substitute for producing the required structure in the first place. Our focus in this book is therefore not on the training of homogeneous neural networks, but on the design of heterogeneous ones. Only once the proper neural architectures for controlling the behavior of autonomous agents have been uncovered can we begin to examine the ways in which the selective introduction of plasticity will increase the flexibility of the resulting controllers.

Finally, most research in artificial neural networks has focused on abstract pattern manipulation tasks. A feedforward network, for example, is used to transform one pattern (e.g. a sequence of words) to another (e.g. a sequence of phonemes). Similarly, a Hopfield network is usually utilized for pattern completion or associative retrieval (e.g. of digitized faces) or for producing a pattern which satisfies some external criterion (e.g. a solution to the traveling salesman problem). Very little work has been done on the design of complete nervous systems which address the entire spectrum of issues involved in controlling the behavior of a whole animal, even a very simple one. Yet this is precisely the *raison d'être* of nervous systems, and our exclusive focus in this book.

3.4 Simulation

An adequate simulation environment is a critical element of this research. The simulator serves as a testbed within which we can examine the behavior of the insect under a variety of environmental conditions. It must be capable of simulating an entire (albeit simple) physical world containing several interacting objects, including insects with multiparted bodies and nervous systems containing on the order of a hundred neurons each. This simulation must be fast enough to allow direct observation of the behavior of artificial insects. In addition, simulation tools must be provided for evaluating and debugging neural controller designs.

The simulator is implemented on a Texas Instruments Explorer II LX Lisp Machine. It consists of approximately 5000 lines of Lisp code. In my experience, the speed of this simulator has ranged from factors of 3 to 10 times slower than real time, depending upon the number, types, and configurations of objects in the environment. While this is far from real time, it has proven sufficient to support an interactive style of use.

The implementation makes heavy use of the object-oriented capabilities of Flavors (Weinreb and Moon, 1980). Object-oriented programming has a number of well-known advantages, including speed of prototyping, clarity of code, and ease of modification. Given the special-purpose nature of the simulation, the ability to mix different models in a single simulation by standardizing the interfaces between them and factoring out the common components via inheritance is particularly important.

Each class of physical object (insects, bricks, and food patches) is represented by a corresponding flavor. These flavors are arranged in an inheritance hierarchy. At the root of this lattice is the flavor **basic-physical-object**. This flavor defines the basic protocol for any physical object. All physical objects have a position, orientation, and bounding circle. In addition, they handle messages for such operations as updating themselves, changing their current position or orientation, and responding to collisions with other physical objects. Specific subclasses of physical objects add additional functionality to this basic set.

Neurons and synapses are also implemented in an object-oriented fashion. However, for efficiency reasons, neurons and synapses are actually represented as Common Lisp structures rather than as flavor instances. This is because message-passing is slower than a normal function call on the TI Explorer II LX. Neurons and synapses are also arranged in inheritance hierarchies. All neurons have a threshold, gain, minimum firing frequency, and list of synapses. Neuron subclasses add a variety of intrinsic currents. For example, a sensory neuron has an additional intrinsic current whose magnitude is an arbitrary Lisp function of some physical quantity such as odor field strength at a given point. In addition, a motor neuron has an arbitrary Lisp function which translates its firing frequency into state changes of some physical object.

The user interface of the simulator is illustrated in Figure 3.9. Its implementation relies heavily upon the predefined window flavors available on the TI Explorer. The interface allows the interactions of multiple insects and other objects to be observed. A simulation may either be run continuously or single-stepped at a variety of timescales. Single-stepping is useful for observing the details of a particular behavior or neural event.

For ease of use, the command interface is menu-driven. Using menus, any physical object may be interactively created, moved, rotated, inspected, or removed from the world, and the parameters of any neuron may be interactively modified. In addition, current of a specified magnitude and duration may be injected into any neuron, and the subsequent behavior of the insect observed. The injection of current is a common technique employed by neurobiologists to explore the operation of a neural circuit.

Finally, the firing frequency, membrane potential, intrinsic currents, and synaptic currents of any neuron may be graphically traced during a running simulation. Again, the use of electrodes to measure currents and voltages is standard practice in neurobiology. The interface therefore supports a style of interaction which is familiar to neurobiologists. Trace panes are also provided for graphically displaying the pattern of movements of an insect's legs or its energy level. All of these capabilities have proven to be important for interactively experimenting with various neural controller designs.

3.5   Related Work

Within AI and related disciplines, there have been a number of research projects aimed at controlling the behavior of autonomous agents embedded in an environment with which they must cope. This section briefly surveys the most relevant of this broadly related work. Work related to more specific issues explored in this book is discussed in the appropriate places.

3.5.1   Planning

As originally conceived in AI, any action taken by an intelligent agent derived from the execution of a plan. Prior to execution, this plan would be constructed from the agent's knowledge of its own capabilities and the

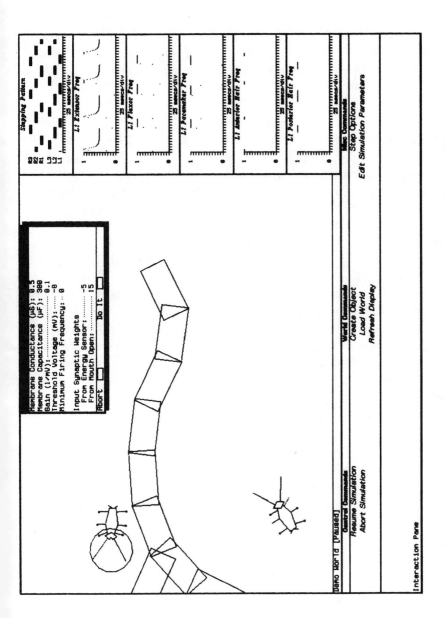

Figure 3.9: The appearance of the screen during a running simulation.

domain in which it operated. This approach made a number of assumptions which are now widely held to be unrealistic for real-world interactions. Ways of making an intelligent agent's behavior more reactive to its immediate situation have been explored by a number of researchers (Maes, 1989; Marks *et al.*, 1989; Firby, 1987; Georgeff and Lansky, 1987; Kaelbling, 1986).

The work of Agre and Chapman is particularly relevant to the approach described in this book (Agre, 1988; Agre and Chapman, 1987). Their work has emphasized the dynamic, improvisatory nature of everyday life, and they have argued that planning as typically formulated in AI is fundamentally intractable for real world situations. Instead of relying on internal representations of the actions to be performed, they have focused on designing internal machinery which can engage in desired routines of activity when placed in the appropriate environmental situation. For this purpose, they make use of purely combinational networks which directly connect perception to action without any intervening state.

To test their ideas, they have built a program called Pengi which controls the behavior of a simple "penguin" embedded within a commercial video arcade game known as Pengo. In this game, bees chase the penguin (which is normally controlled by a person via a joystick) through a two dimensional maze which can be modified by kicking the ice blocks out of which it is constructed. The bees attempt to kill the penguin by either stinging it or kicking an ice block into it, while the penguin attempts to evade the bees by running or rearranging the maze, and to kill them with ice blocks. While this is clearly a toy domain in one sense, Agre and Chapman argue that it is utterly unlike those typically chosen in AI. The world in which the penguin must perform consists of hundreds of objects and it must quickly adapt its behavior to constantly changing circumstances.

3.5.2 Robotics

Within robotics, there is a great deal of interest in building autonomous mobile robots which can flexibly cope with unanticipated contingencies in complex, dynamic environments. It has become clear that much of the classical AI planning approaches to this problem are hopelessly intractable and brittle when confronted with the open-endedness, unpredictability, and real-time constraints of the real world. Therefore, a number of researchers have begun to explore new architectures for the control of autonomous robots which emphasize rapid reaction to changing conditions (Arkin, 1989;

Payton, 1986).

The work of Brooks is perhaps most similar in spirit to the approach taken in this book. Brooks has also criticized AI for emphasizing narrow and rigid expertise over the more basic skills required to simply survive in the real world (Brooks, 1987). He has suggested that the classical methodology has been used to abstract away the most fundamental problems in AI. He advocates instead the building of robots which are capable of simple, robust, and adaptive behaviors in unconstrained environments. To control these robots, Brooks makes use of a layered control system called the *subsumption architecture* (Brooks, 1986). It is based upon finite state machines augmented by internal registers and timers. Each layer is organized around a particular task, such as object avoidance or exploration. Higher level behaviors are built upon the abilities of lower layers. This approach has been applied to the construction of robots which explore, follow objects, and walk (Brooks, 1989; Horswill and Brooks, 1988; Connell, 1987). Brooks' approach differs from the one taken in this book in its choice of agent (physical robot vs. simulated insect), control scheme (networks of augmented finite state machines vs. neural networks), and degree of biological inspiration.

3.5.3 Neural Networks and Connectionism

Using networks of simple logic threshold devices (McCullough and Pitts, 1943), Braitenberg has proposed a series of robots known as *vehicles* (Braitenberg, 1984). These robots were to be capable of a variety of simple behaviors such as seeking out light and avoiding each other. This idea builds on a long cybernetic tradition (Walter, 1950).

Inspired by Braitenberg's proposal, Travers has constructed a simulation environment which allowed point-like vehicles to interact with food and obstacles (Travers, 1988a). Travers also developed an ethological simulation strategy known as AGAR, which allows the interactive assembly of artificial animals. Based upon Minsky's Society of Mind Theory (Minsky, 1985), AGAR represents each possible behavior as an *agent* which can be activated or deactivated by conditions in the environment, other agents, or timers. Using AGAR, Travers developed a simulation of food recruitment in ants (Travers, 1988b). In a similar vein, Coderre constructed a simulation known as PETWORLD (Coderre, 1988). The behavior of "pets" in this world is controlled by hierarchical experts which are also inspired by Minsky's theories.

Hood has proposed the development of a series of artificial organisms in order to explore the neural bases of autonomous, goal-based learning (Hood, 1985; Hood, 1986). He was interested in several forms of learning, including habituation, sensitization, classical conditioning, and operant conditioning. Each organism was to be controlled by an artificially designed nervous system based upon organizational principles found in simpler natural organisms. The performance of these organisms were to be tested in a realistic simulated environment known as the World Modeling System (Hood and Carbonell, 1982).

Arbib has constructed a family of models of visually-guided behavior in frogs and toads known as *Rana computatrix* (Arbib, 1982; Arbib, 1987). These models combine ethological and neurobiological data with Arbib's notion of a *schema* to provide accounts for such behaviors as prey selection and prey catching. The accounts are backed up by simulation results from simplified models of the relevant neural circuitry.

Edelman has synthesized data from a great variety of sources into his theory of neuronal group selection (Edelman, 1987). He argues that the world does not come prelabeled into particular categories which are directly represented in the brain. Rather, an animal must form the appropriate categories itself, and constantly update them as it confronts it environment. He proposes a mechanism for this which is based upon the idea that groups of neurons undergo a selection process similar to that operating on populations of organisms in evolution. Simulations of this theory have demonstrated the ability to carry out simple categorization and association tasks in novel environments. In the most recent simulation, categorization is combined with motor control capabilities to produce a simple organism capable of adaptively interacting with its environment (Reeke and Edelman, 1988).

3.5.4   Genetic Algorithms

Within the genetic algorithm literature, there has been some interest in evolving collections of stereotyped production rules known as *classifiers* to control the behavior of simple organisms (typically, single points). Wilson described a classifier-based organism that learned to find food and avoid obstacles in a two-dimensional world (Wilson, 1985; Wilson, 1987). In a similar vein, Booker has described a classifier system which learns internal world models of its environment (Booker, 1988). It uses these models to locate food and avoid painful stimuli. More sophisticated ecological simulations, in which populations of point-like organisms interact and evolve in a simulated ecosystem, include EVOLVE III (Rizki and Conrad, 1986) and RAM (Taylor *et al.*, 1988).

Chapter 4

Locomotion

4.1 Introduction

An animal's ability to traverse its environment is fundamental to many of its other behaviors. In most insects, this requirement is fulfilled by six-legged walking. Locomotion is also an interesting adaptive behavior in its own right. An insect robustly solves this complex coordination problem in real time in the presence of variations in load and terrain, developmental changes, and damage to its walking apparatus.

For these reasons, locomotion was the first behavior provided to *P. computatrix*. Because this insect can fall down, its locomotion controller must properly coordinate the movements of the insect's six legs in order to produce successful walking. The insect must also be able to walk at a variety of different speeds while maintaining the stability of its body. In addition, the locomotion controller must be robust enough that small perturbations (such as those caused by a collision with a brick or wall) will not seriously disrupt it.

4.2 Neuroethological Background

The design of the locomotion controller utilized in *P. computatrix* was inspired by work on the neuroethology of insect locomotion, which has recently been reviewed by Graham (1985). While no complete neural circuit has been worked out for the walking of any animal, a considerable amount

71

is known about the reflex effects and overall organization of the locomotion controllers of some insects. This section briefly summarizes the relevant aspects of this work, focusing entirely on terrestrial, hexapod locomotion.

During normal terrestrial walking, hexapod insects always maintain static equilibrium: at any given point in time, there are sufficiently many legs available to support the body. In a walking insect, individual legs may be in one of two phases. In the *stance phase*, a leg is on the ground and swinging back, providing both support and propulsive forces to the body. During the *swing phase*, a leg is off the ground and swinging forward and is therefore unavailable for support. Because a limited number of legs are simultaneously being used for both support and progression, a coordination problem immediately arises. A particularly strong constraint is placed upon the timing of the initiation of a swing phase, because no leg must swing until a sufficient number of other legs are supporting the body. The timing of this switch from stance to swing has been shown to be affected by such factors as the load carried by a leg, its position, and the relative phases of other legs.

Certain patterns of leg movements or *gaits* will be capable of continuously maintaining static stability and others will not. The gaits of many animals, including insects, often exhibit a particular stepping sequence known as the *metachronal wave*, in which a wave of swings progresses from the rear of the animal to its front. In insects, for example, the back leg swings, then the middle leg, then the front leg on each side of the body. As the speed of walking varies, this basic pattern remains on each side of the body, but the relative phase of the two waves across the body changes (Wilson, 1966). Thus, at very low speeds of walking, the two waves may be completely separated, resulting in the so-called *wave gait*. At high speeds of walking, on the other hand, the two waves may overlap completely, producing the so-called *tripod gait* in which the front and back legs on one side of the body swing in unison with the middle leg on the opposite side. These gaits are illustrated in Figure 4.5, to which we will return later in this chapter.

Wilson (1966) has argued that all six-legged insect gaits can be accounted for by the following five rules:

1. A wave of swings progresses from back to front, with no leg swinging until the one behind is providing support.

2. Opposite legs of the same segment alternate in phase.

3. The duration of the swing phase is relatively constant.

4. The duration of the stance phases decreases as step frequency increases.

5. The time between swings of the hindleg and middle leg and between the middle leg and the foreleg are relatively constant, while the interval between foreleg and hindleg steps varies inversely with step frequency.

Pearson and his colleagues have extensively studied the neural basis of locomotion in the American cockroach (Pearson, 1976a; Pearson *et al.*, 1973). This work has led to the development of a model for the overall organization of the local leg circuitry underlying cockroach locomotion (Figure 4.1). At the center of this model is a central pattern generator whose bursts of activity excite motor neurons responsible for the swing phase and inhibit those responsible for the stance phase. While the neural circuitry comprising this pattern generator remains unknown, nonspiking interneurons have been identified which appear to be members of this pattern generator. This pattern generator operates against a background of steady excitation descending from higher brain centers, which also excite the pattern generator itself.

The central pattern generator underlying the rhythmic movements of each leg is shaped by feedback from two sensory structures. Tiny hairs near the leg joints which are stimulated when the leg has reached its extreme forward position have been shown to inhibit the CPG and the swing motor neurons and excite the motor neurons controlling stance. These hairs thus appear to play a role in controlling the switch from swing to stance.

Sensory structures which measure stress in the legs have also been shown to influence locomotion in two ways. First, their stimulation can prevent activity in the pattern generator, and thus may play a role in controlling the switch from stance to swing by preventing a heavily loaded leg from swinging. Second, these sensory structures excite stance motor neurons, providing a possible mechanism for load compensation.

How are the pattern generators controlling each individual leg coupled to produce statically stable gaits? Both intersegmental and intrasegmental inhibitory interactions between the pattern generators of individual legs have been identified. This has led Pearson to propose that the pattern generators of all adjacent legs mutually inhibit one another.

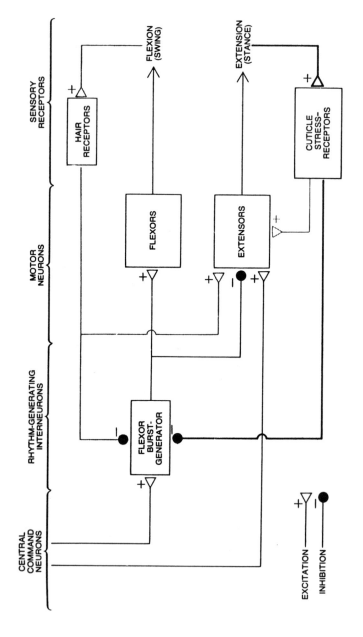

Figure 4.1: Pearson's flexor burst-generator model for cockroach locomotion. (Illustration by Alan D. Iselin from *The Control of Walking*, by Keir Pearson, *Scientific American*, Vol. 235, No. 6, p. 85.)

4.3   Leg Controller

The most basic components of walking are the rhythmic movements of each individual leg. In *P. computatrix*, these rhythmic movements are produced by the leg controller network shown in Figure 4.2.[1] The single command neuron *LC* replaces the descending commands from higher brain centers in Pearson's model. There are six copies of the remainder of this circuit, one for each leg. *LC* makes the same two connections to each of the individual leg controllers.

The basic rhythmic movements of each leg are produced by the central pattern generator shown in solid lines in Figure 4.2. This circuitry comes fairly directly from Pearson's model. His unknown pattern generation circuitry has been replaced by a single pacemaker neuron *P*. Each leg is controlled by three motor neurons. The *stance* and *swing* motor neurons determine the force with which the leg is swung backward or forward, respectively. When its foot is down, such forces translate the body forward or backward, respectively. For straight-line locomotion, rotations due to differential forces across the body are ignored. The foot motor neuron controls whether the foot is up or down.

Normally, the *foot* motor neuron is active and the stance motor neuron is excited by the command neuron *LC*. This puts the foot down and pushes the leg back, producing a stance phase. Periodically, however, this state is interrupted by a burst from the pacemaker neuron *P*. This burst inhibits the foot and stance motor neurons and excites the swing motor neuron, producing a swing phase. When this burst terminates, another stance phase begins. Rhythmic bursting in *P* thus produces the basic swing/stance cycle required for walking. Corresponding to Pearson's model, the force applied during each stance phase, as well as the time between bursts in *P*, depends upon the level of excitation supplied by the command neuron *LC*.

In order to properly time the transitions between the swing and stance phases, the leg controllers must have some information about where the legs actually are. The connections which provide this sensory information are shown with dashed lines in Figure 4.2. These sensors serve to reinforce and fine-tune the centrally generated stepping rhythm. When a leg is all the way forward, the *forward angle sensor* encourages *P* to terminate its current burst by inhibiting it. This sensor plays the same role as the hair receptors

---

[1] Here and throughout the main body of the text, only a circuit diagram and a qualitative description of the dynamics underlying the operation of each neural controller are provided. More detailed specifications of these circuits can be found in Appendix B.

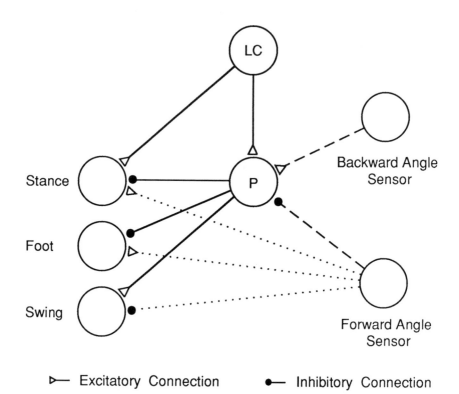

▷— Excitatory Connection   ●— Inhibitory Connection

Figure 4.2: Leg Controller Circuit. The neurons along the left side of
the diagram are motor neurons which control the leg. The neurons along
the right side of the diagram are sensory neurons. P is a pacemaker cell,
a neuron whose firing frequency varies rhythmically. LC is a command
neuron which is shared by all of the leg controllers. Excitatory connections
are shown as open triangles and inhibitory connections are shown as closed
circles. The basic central pattern generator is shown in solid lines. Dashed
lines represent sensory feedback. Connections comprising the stance reflex
are shown with dotted lines.

in Pearson's model, limiting the extent of a swing and contributing to the switch from swing to stance.

When a leg is all the way back, the *backward angle sensor* encourages P to initiate a swing by exciting it. This sensor is related to the stress receptors in Pearson's model. However, the correspondence is not nearly as direct as for the forward angle sensor. The stress receptors are essentially load sensors, while the backward angle sensor is a position sensor. A variety of load sensors were experimented with, but with largely unsatisfactory results. This may have been due to the difficulty of capturing the three-dimensional load distribution of a walking insect in a two-dimensional model. However, it may also suggest that load information alone is not sufficient for controlling the switch from swing to stance. In at least one hexapod robot (Donner, 1987), the direct use of leg load information to control swing phase initiation produced very irregular stepping patterns even for flat, horizontal surfaces. Leg position is known to play an important role in controlling the switch from stance to swing for the cat (Pearson, 1976a) and the stick insect (Graham, 1985). At any rate, the role played by the backward angle sensors is essentially identical to that played by the cuticle stress receptors in Pearson's model when normal locomotion across flat, horizontal terrain is considered. Both sensors encourage swing phase initiation when a leg is nearing its extreme backward position.

Finally, the dotted connections in Figure 4.2 implement the hair receptor reflexes in Pearson's model. This stance reflex serves to smooth the transition from swing to stance because it gives the motor neurons a slight kick in the right direction to begin a stance phase whenever the leg is swung all the way forward. The leg controller circuit does not include the load compensation reflex involving the cuticle stress receptors in Pearson's model.

4.4 Locomotion Controller

In order for these six individual leg controllers to form a locomotion controller, we must address the issue of stability. Because the insect can fall down, arbitrary patterns of leg movements will not, in general, lead to successful walking. The movements of the individual legs must be synchronized in such a way as to continuously maintain the stability of the body.

One good rule of thumb is that adjacent legs should be discouraged from swinging at the same time. If the front and middle legs on one side of

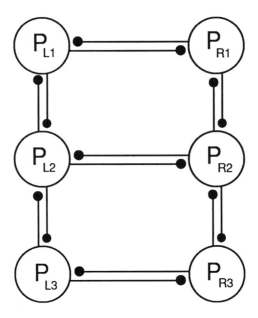

Figure 4.3: Inhibitory coupling between the pacemakers of each leg.

the body were to swing simultaneously, for example, the likelihood of the insect becoming statically unstable is high. As shown in Figure 4.3, this constraint was implemented by mutual inhibition between the pacemakers of adjacent legs. This coupling scheme is derived from Pearson's model.

This inhibitory coupling produces the tripod gait at high speeds of walking. At lower speeds of walking, however, these constraints are not sufficient to guarantee the reliable production of statically stable gaits. In particular, *P. computatrix* does not exhibit the metachronal waves observed in the slower gaits of insects and many other natural animals. Instead, the stepping patterns it produces during slow walks depend in general upon the initial conditions of the legs.

In order to enforce the generation of metachronal waves, the following idea from Graham (1977) was utilized. If the burst frequency of the rear pacemakers is lowered relative to the other ones, phase-locking can occur between them. The rear pacemakers will entrain the middle and front ones in such a way as to produce metachronal waves. In *P. computatrix*, the burst frequency of the rear pacemakers was lowered by slightly increasing the angle ranges of the rear legs, so that they swing farther back than the middle or front legs before a swing phase is initiated.

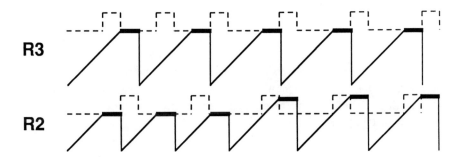

Figure 4.4: Phase-locking of two coupled oscillators in generating a metachronal wave. A heavy line represents the burst of an oscillator. A dotted line represents the time at which an oscillator's interburst interval terminates, which is increased when that oscillator experiences inhibition due to a burst in the other oscillator. Solid lines represent the progress of an oscillator toward the time of its next burst. The slower oscillator, $R3$, begins in phase with the faster oscillator, $R2$. However, $R3$'s inhibition acts to slow R2 sufficiently to entrain it after several cycles, resulting in a metachronal burst sequence in which a burst in $R3$ is immediately followed by a burst in $R2$.

The process of phase-locking is illustrated in Figure 4.4 for the case of two mutually inhibitory abstract oscillators, which can be thought of as representing the pacemakers for the back ($R3$) and middle ($R2$) legs on the right side of the body. Each oscillator can be described as counting at a fixed rate toward some final value. When this threshold value is reached, the oscillator bursts for some fixed period of time, and then resets, beginning its count anew. In the figure, both oscillators count at the same rate. However, oscillator $R3$ has been made to burst at a somewhat lower frequency than $R2$ by slightly raising its threshold.

If $R2$ and $R3$ were uncoupled, there may be no fixed phase relationship between them. However, because they are coupled by mutual inhibition, a burst in one oscillator has the effect of temporarily raising the threshold for bursting of the other oscillator, potentially prolonging its interburst interval. If the ratio between the interburst intervals of the two oscillators is set appropriately, the inhibition from the slower oscillator ($R3$) eventually "catches" the faster one ($R2$), slowing it down and locking it into a metachronal phase relationship in which each burst in $R3$ is immediately followed by a burst in $R2$.

This intuitive explanation illustrates the basic idea behind the phase-locking responsible for the metachronal wave in the locomotion controller. The full explanation is somewhat more complex than this, due to the voltage and time dependencies of the intrinsic currents underlying the rhythmic bursting of the pacemaker neurons, their RC characteristics, and the sensory feedback that they receive. The role of some of these effects will be explored in Chapter 5.

The entrainment responsible for the metachronal wave can break down for too slow a walk or too fast a change in speed. In order to ensure that this does not occur, the command neuron LC was given a nonzero minimum firing frequency and a large capacitance. The minimum firing frequency was set so that the slowest possible walk is still one in which the entrainment is stable. The large capacitance ensures that any change in speed (initiated by a change in the level of excitation or inhibition provided to the command neuron) is spread over a number of steps.

4.5   Results

When this controller is embedded in the body of *P. computatrix*, it reliably produces successful walking. The insect can be made to exhibit a variety of statically stable gaits simply by varying the firing frequency of the command neuron LC. Observed gaits range from ones in which the metachronal waves on each side of the body are very nearly separated to the tripod gait, in which the front and back legs on each side of the body step with the middle leg on the opposite side. These stepping patterns emerge from the interaction between the dynamics of the locomotion controller and the body in which it is embedded (see next chapter). The gaits are stable in the sense that small perturbations either in the initial conditions, to the locomotion controller, or to the legs themselves do not serve to destroy them.

If the legs are labeled as shown at the top of Figure 4.5, then gaits may be conveniently described by their footfall patterns. In this representation, a black bar is displayed during the swing phase of each leg. The space between bars represents the stance phase. Selected gaits observed in *P.*

computatrix at different speeds of walking are shown at the right of Figure 4.5 as the command neuron firing frequency is varied from lowest to highest by the external injection of current.

As shown at the left of Figure 4.5, the sequence of gaits exhibited by P. computatrix bears a strong resemblance to those that have been described by Wilson (1966) for natural insects. At the lower speeds, the metachronal waves on each side of the body are very apparent. The metachronal waves can still be discerned in faster walks. However, they increasingly overlap as the stance phases shorten, until the tripod gait appears. Though only four different gaits are shown for *P. computatrix*, corresponding to four discrete firing frequencies of the command neuron LC, a continuum of gaits is possible. Figure 4.6 shows a gait transition from the tripod gait to a slower gait which illustrates this continuum. This transition occurs over several steps due to the large time constant of the command neuron.

P. computatrix does not exhibit either the slowest (a) or fastest (f) insect gaits. At the slow walking speeds required for gait (a), the entrainment responsible for the metachronal wave breaks down. At the fast walking speeds required for gait (f), interference between bursts in adjacent pacemakers leads to uncoordinated stepping patterns. It is interesting to note that neither of these gaits have been observed in the American cockroach, though they have both been observed in other insects. In fact, it appears that the *P. americana* normally utilizes only gaits (d) and (e) (Delcomyn, 1971).

The ability of this controller to generate a significant fraction of insect gaits, and continuous transitions between them, simply by varying the tonic activity of a single neuron was a somewhat unexpected result. Although the controller was based on Pearson's model for cockroach locomotion (with the addition of a mechanism for producing metachronal waves), no aspect of its design was explicitly motivated by a desire to reproduce these properties of insect locomotion. This is the first of several examples in the design of the artificial insect where a little extra attention to biological details resulted in unexpected payoffs.

The neural activity in the front left leg controller during a typical slower gait is shown in Figure 4.7. Note the correspondence between a pacemaker burst, a burst in the swing motor neuron, and the swing bar for $L1$ in the stepping pattern. The sharp spike at the beginning of each burst in the stance motor neuron is caused by the stance reflex. It can be seen to correspond to activity in the forward angle sensor.

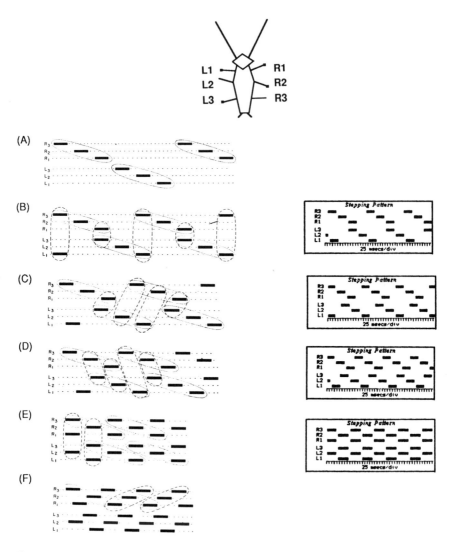

Figure 4.5: A comparison between the gaits of *P. computatrix* and those observed in natural insects. (Top) Leg labeling conventions. In the stepping pattern displays, solid bars indicate swing phases and the space between bars represents stance phases. (Left) A description of the gaits observed in natural insects (Reproduced, with permission, from the *Annual Review of Entomology*, Volume 11. ©1966 by Annual Reviews Inc.). (Right) Selected gaits observed in *P. computatrix* as the firing frequency of the command neuron LC is varied from lowest (top) to highest (bottom). Note the metachronal waves in all gaits.

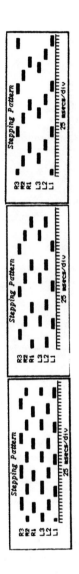

Figure 4.6: Stepping patterns occurring during a gait transition from the tripod gait to a slower gait.

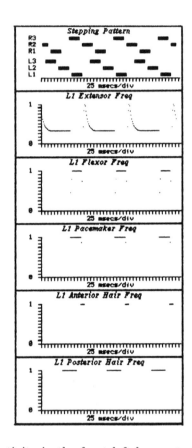

Figure 4.7: Neural activity in the front left leg controller during a typical gait. From top to bottom, the traces show the stepping pattern, and the corresponding firing frequency of the stance motor neuron (here labeled *L1 Extensor*), the swing motor neuron (here labeled *L1 Flexor*), the pacemaker, the forward angle sensor, and the backward angle sensor.

4.6 Neuroethological Significance

Though a great many simplifications have been made, the locomotion controller of *P. computatrix* remains faithful to a number of the neuroethological facts concerning cockroach walking. Despite the fact that this was not its original motivation, it is interesting to briefly consider the significance of this controller as a model of insect locomotion.

Perhaps the most important result of the locomotion controller is its ability to reproduce such a range of normal insect gaits simply by varying a single tonic command signal. To my knowledge, the ability of Pearson's model, which was largely derived from experimental data, to produce the tripod gait had never been verified. By making reasonable assumptions regarding the neural encoding of some of the black boxes in his model, the locomotion controller developed above demonstrates that it can indeed account for this high-speed gait.

A more interesting result is that the model could not account for the slower gaits which are sometimes observed in cockroaches without additional mechanisms. It was certainly not clear from published descriptions of Pearson's model that this was so. Of course, this negative result may only reflect the fact that the locomotion controller is an insufficiently realistic representation of the neural circuitry. At any rate, it does suggest that Pearson's model will need to be fleshed out in more detail before its ability to account for slower gaits can be fully evaluated.

In order to produce the metachronal waves which appear to be lacking in Pearson's model, the locomotion controller utilizes a specific mechanism for phase-locking the pacemakers on each side of the body. It is difficult to assess the relevance of this mechanism for insect locomotion. To the extent that the pattern generators of each segment are indeed coupled by inhibition, as Pearson's model suggests, the mechanism is at least plausible. It is also testable, at least in principle, by comparing the natural frequency of an isolated rear pattern generator to that of a middle or front one.

When assessing any model, it is important to examine not only its ability to mimic the normal operation of the actual system, but also to compare their responses to perturbations. The next chapter describes in considerable detail a series of lesion studies of the locomotion controller. Only those results of particular relevance to the current discussion are summarized here.

One interesting similarity between the model and the animal involves the response to removal of the hair receptors (forward angle sensor in the model). In both the animal and the model, this lesion produces a prolonged swing phase, with the lesioned leg swinging much farther forward than normal (Wong and Pearson, 1976). Thus this sensory information appears to be crucial to properly timing the transition between swing and stance.

When the endogenous oscillations of the central pattern generators are disabled by strongly inhibiting the locomotion command neuron, another interesting similarity is observed. If the insect is pushed along at the appropriate speed by some external force, it still exhibits the full range of normal gaits. Apparently the sensory information alone is sufficient to properly coordinate the legs under these conditions. This *reflex stepping* has been observed in a variety of animals after the removal of higher control centers (Grillner, 1981).

These and other lesions of the model have demonstrated that the interactions between the sensory and central components of the locomotion controller are subtle and complex. In many cases, sensory information can at least partially compensate for central lesions, and vice versa. In addition, the relative importance of these two components varies for the different gaits. In general, it appears that sensory information is most important for the slower gaits and least important for the fastest gaits, which are primarily generated centrally. Zill (1985) has reached the same conclusions for cockroach locomotion. The relationship between central and peripheral components in insect locomotion in particular and pattern generation in general is currently a topic of some controversy in neurobiology (Pearson, 1985). The extreme subtlety of the central/peripheral interactions in even this simple artificial insect suggests why this is such a difficult issue to resolve.

One expected but significant failure of the model is its inability to account for the results of leg amputation experiments in insects. It is well-known that insects can immediately adapt their gaits to compensate for the amputation of one or two legs (Graham, 1985). In fact, an insect's normal response to leg damage is self-amputation. In contrast, leg amputations in *P. computatrix* generally lead to statically unstable gaits. In natural insects, it appears that the pattern of load carried by the remaining legs can modify the gait so as to compensate for a missing leg. Given that load plays no role in the locomotion controller described here, it therefore comes as no surprise that it fails to compensate in a similar manner.

Despite some very suggestive parallels, the locomotion of *P. computatrix* possesses a number of limitations which must be rectified in order to further pursue its use as a neural model of cockroach locomotion. For example, it is known that swing phase duration is not constant, but does in fact decrease somewhat as walking speed increases. This fact could be incorporated into the model by making the I_H intrinsic pacemaker current voltage-dependent as well. In addition, the actual three-dimensional structure of cockroach legs and their movement during locomotion is significantly more complex than that of *P. computatrix*. A more realistic body model would also allow for the proper computation of the loads carried by each leg. Perhaps most importantly of all, a considerably deeper understanding of the pattern generation circuitry responsible for locomotion in the cockroach must be attained before a significantly more realistic model could be constructed.

4.7 Related Work

The construction of machines capable of legged locomotion has long been an area of considerable interest. Legged locomotion offers a number of advantages over more conventional forms of transportation, including the ability to travel across terrain inaccessible to wheeled and tracked vehicles and the decoupling of the path of the body and the path of the feet, which allows the body to travel smoothly despite large variations in terrain. In general, work in this area has focused on the problems inherent in building and controlling such vehicles. Most of the control algorithms which have been developed are centralized and computationally expensive (Donner, 1987). Often, the mechanical design is chosen so as to reduce the number of degrees of freedom which must be controlled (Song and Waldron, 1989). Such work is too far afield to describe in any detail here. Surveys can be found in (Raibert, 1989), (Song and Waldron, 1989) and (Todd, 1985). However, two recent efforts in this area are particularly relevant to the distributed approach described above.

Donner (1987) used a distributed system for controlling the locomotion of a statically stable, hydraulically-actuated, six-legged robot. Each leg was controlled by a separate process, written in a concurrent language known as OWL, which was responsible for the basic swing/stance cycle. A critical component of these processes was the decision to switch from stance to swing. A leg which had reached the end of its travel was allowed to swing only if the load it was carrying was below some threshold value. Coordination was achieved by three mechanisms, all of which involved the manipulation of this threshold. While a leg was swinging, it lowered the load threshold of adjacent legs. In addition, a leg which had just completed its swing would raise the threshold of the leg in front of it. Finally, each rear leg raised the load threshold of the other when it reached the middle of its stance. These mechanisms were meant to encourage the development of metachronal waves and were based on early models of insect walking due to Wilson (1966). However, although the hexapod successfully walked, it did not generally exhibit metachronal waves. Donner also demonstrated the ability of this controller to compensate for a missing leg.

Brooks (1989) has described a semi-distributed locomotion controller for an insect-like autonomous robot. The legs were controlled by a network of 57 finite state machines augmented by registers and timers. These machines interacted by sending messages. The swing/stance cycle of each leg is driven by a chain of peripheral reflexes using only coarse, local information about leg load and position. The robot successfully walked with a variety of different gaits, could negotiate small obstacles, and follow slowly moving objects using infrared sensors. Coordination between legs was achieved by a central leg lift sequencer which was modified in order to produce the different gaits.

Another example of related work comes from the area of computer animation. There is currently considerable interest in the use of forward dynamic simulation to bring added realism to the animation of articulated figures such as animals and human beings. McKenna and Zeltzer (1989) have developed a technique for realistically animating the locomotion of a cockroach. Their three-dimensional body model contained 27 subparts with 39 total degrees of freedom and was simulated using realistic Newtonian dynamics. Each leg was controlled by *dynamic motor programs* for stance and swing which were driven by a sine wave. The gait patterns described by Wilson (1966) for insects were translated into velocity-dependent phase relationships between the sine waves controlling each leg. In addition, the individual motor programs were modified by information about the position of a leg and its importance to the stability of the body, and the state of other legs. The overall organization of these dynamic motor programs was also inspired by Pearson's work (1976a).

Chapter 5

Lesion Studies[1]

5.1 Motivation

The existence of a distributed, heterogeneous neural network such as the locomotion controller described in the previous chapter raises two important and interrelated questions. (1) How robust is it? In order for a neural controller to have any claim to being adaptive, it must be capable of functioning in the presence of a variety of perturbations. (2) How does it work? The locomotion controller, for example, was designed using a combination of biological inspiration and common sense intuition. It is not at all clear how its various components actually contribute to the generation of the different gaits it produces. Both the robustness and function questions can only be answered by a detailed analysis of the neural controller itself.

The analysis of a heterogeneous neural network poses special difficulties, since it contains a variety of elements with unique intrinsic properties connected in a nonuniform manner. One approach that has been employed in the analysis of more homogeneous artificial neural networks involves the use of random perturbations: randomly removing or changing the signs of connections, randomly eliminating neural elements entirely, or transiently altering the activity of selected elements of the network. The degradation of the performance of the network is then measured as a function of such

[1] ©1989 IEEE. Adapted, with permission, from *A Lesion Study of a Heterogeneous Artificial Neural Network for Hexapod Locomotion*, by H.J. Chiel and R.D. Beer, *Proceedings of the First International Joint Conference on Neural Networks, (Washington D.C., June 18-22, 1989), pp. 407-414.*

perturbations. One of the attractions of artificial neural networks has been the observation that such perturbations generally cause a graceful degradation of function rather than an abrupt failure (Hopfield, 1982; McClelland, 1986; Sejnowski and Rosenberg, 1987). Random perturbations are an effective tool for analysis because these networks are homogeneous. Although these techniques may also be appropriate for analyzing a heterogeneous neural network, they do not clarify the role of the different elements in its operation.

Neurobiologists probe biological nervous systems using several classes of perturbation. One class involves the removal of specific parts of the system. This can be accomplished by removing parts of the animal's body, by severing connections between neurons, or by injecting inhibitory current into a nerve cell and preventing it from firing. Such perturbations are generally referred to as *lesions*. A second class of perturbations is the activation of specific parts of the system in an abnormal fashion. Examples of this class include forcing a normally phasic sensory receptor (i.e., one that bursts rhythmically) into tonic activity (i.e., bursting continuously). A third class of perturbations is the reversible alteration of the intrinsic properties of or connections between nerve cells. Such alterations are generally accomplished by the application of drugs. Finally, the activity of certain elements may be transiently perturbed by injecting a brief pulse of current, and the subsequent response of the network can then be observed. These observations lead to specific hypotheses about the function of different parts of the network, which are in turn tested by other perturbations.

This chapter examines the effects of similar perturbations on the function of the locomotion controller described in Chapter 4. Because the perturbations employed primarily involve the removal of neurons or connections, this examination is called a *lesion study*. To repeat, this lesion study was undertaken in order to explore two related questions regarding this controller: (1) How robust is the ability of the locomotion controller to generate statically stable gaits? and (2) What are the relative roles of the various components of the locomotion controller in generating normal gaits?

5.2 Perturbation Methods

The user interface of the simulator makes it possible to perturb the controller rather easily. Because the simulation can be single-stepped, the

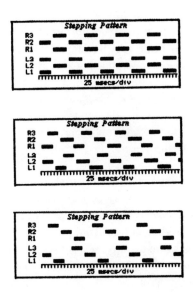

Figure 5.1: Normal low (bottom), medium (middle), and high (top) speed gaits.

timing of perturbations can be fairly precise. In addition, the ability to interactively inject current into any neuron and to edit its parameters greatly simplifies the lesions themselves. Neurons were removed from the controller by injecting large hyperpolarizing currents into them, and connections were removed by zeroing the appropriate connection weights.

In all of the experiments reported here, the initial leg positions were randomized before each run. In addition, the membrane potentials of all neurons were initialized to zero. In general, the response of the controller to a given lesion is sensitive both to the speed of walking and the gait utilized. Three different walking speeds (referred to as low, medium, and high) were examined. These correspond to three different levels of current injection into the locomotion command neuron, LC. In the normal controller, these activation levels lead to three distinct gaits (Figure 5.1).

The following terminology was adopted for assessing the responses of $P.$ $computatrix$ to lesions. A $normal$ gait is one which is essentially identical to that observed in the unlesioned controller for the same level of current injection. Any gait which is not normal is termed *abnormal.* A gait which continuously maintains the static stability of the body is called a *statically stable* gait. A gait which exhibits periods of static instability which are too brief to result in falling down is called *marginally statically stable.* Finally, any gait which results in the insect periodically falling down is called *statically unstable.* In addition to evaluating the extent to which a particular gait maintains the static stability of the body, the stability of the gait itself to small perturbations is also discussed.

5.3   Robustness

In preparation for each experiment, a normal insect was allowed to walk at an intermediate speed for several steps until transients had died out and a stable gait was established. When slower or faster gaits were studied, an appropriate current was then injected into the locomotion command neuron, and the insect was again allowed several steps to establish a new stable gait. Finally, the lesion was performed and the subsequent response of the insect was studied. The effects of lesions occurring during the transients, before stable gaits were established, were not examined.

5.3.1   Sensory Lesions

In general, the controller was found to be fairly robust to a variety of sensory lesions. The effects of removing the forward angle sensors, which initiate the switch from swing to stance via both pacemaker inhibition and the stance reflex, were first explored (Figure 5.2). Lesions of single or of all forward angle sensors occasionally produced abnormal gaits, but never resulted in the insect falling down. At medium speed, removing either a single forward angle sensor or all of them had no effect. The insect exhibited normal, marginally statically stable gaits at high speeds. In the tripod gait, this marginal stability is caused by the occasional overlap of the slightly longer than normal swing phases due to the missing stance reflexes (Figure 5.3). The largest gait abnormality was observed when all forward angle sensors were removed after the slowest gait had been established. The insect was initially statically unstable, but the gait slowly changed over many steps and finally settled into an abnormal pattern which did not exhibit the metachronal wave, but was statically stable.

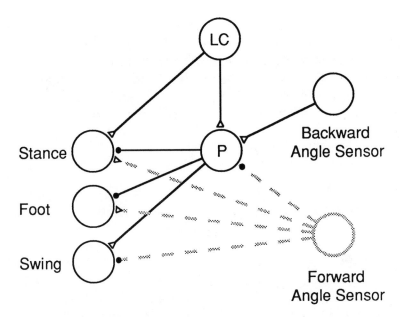

Figure 5.2: A forward angle sensor lesion. Note that this lesion removes both a source of sensory feedback and the stance reflex.

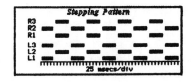

Figure 5.3: (Top) A normal tripod gait. (Bottom) After lesion of the forward angle sensor of leg L1. Note longer swing bar for L1.

The effects of removing the backward angle sensors, which excite the pacemakers and thus contribute to the initiation of the swing phase, were then explored. At the fastest gait, removing one or all of these sensors had little effect. It seems that the tonic excitation from the command neuron and the phasic *absence* of inhibition from the other pacemakers provide sufficient constraints for the tripod gait. At slower speeds, removing backward angle sensors caused greater disruption. Gaits were either abnormal but statically stable, or statically unstable.

5.3.2   Central Lesions

The effects of lesioning two classes of central connections were explored next: (1) those from the command neuron to the pacemakers, and (2) those between pacemakers. Removing single connections from the command neuron to the pacemakers had no effect on gaits at any speed. It was somewhat surprising to find that removing *all* connections from the command neuron to the pacemakers also had no effect. These lesions, like the others described in this section, were imposed once normal gaits had been established. As discussed later (Section 5.4.3), such lesions do have a significant impact when applied before normal gaits are established.

The inhibitory connections between pacemakers are designed to provide decentralized coordination of their relative phases. Since adjacent pacemakers mutually inhibit one another, there are a total of 14 such connections. These connections are clearly essential for the formation of normal gaits. It was found that lesioning all of these connections led to statically unstable gaits at all speeds. However, lesioning fewer connections produced more subtle effects.

As discussed above, the random removal of connections has been a popular analysis technique for homogeneous neural networks. Because the pattern of coordinating inhibition between pacemakers appears to be the most homogeneous part of this controller, the technique of random lesions was applied to these connections. Lesioning any one of these connections had no effect on the ability of the controller to generate stable gaits at any speed.

Randomly removing 50% of the coordinating inhibitory connections had different effects at different speeds. At the highest speed, the insect became unstable 80% of the time (25 trials). In the case of medium speed walks, the insect became unstable 40% of the time (25 trials). For the lowest speed, the insect became unstable 64% of the time (25 trials). The probability of failure for random removal of from 0 to 9 coordinating connections between pacemakers is shown in Figure 5.4.

5.3.3 Motor Lesions

As would be expected, lesioning swing motor neurons produced disastrous results because the affected legs could never be recovered from stance. Lesions of foot motor neurons were similarly devastating. In this case, the lesioned legs were unable to provide any support to the body. Functionally, such lesions correspond to the removal of a leg. The locomotion controller is therefore not able to adjust its gaits to compensate for leg amputations.

Lesioning single stance motor neurons did not lead to statically unstable gaits. At medium and high speeds, lesioning single stance motor neurons led to normal, statically stable gaits. However, the insect's forward velocity was slightly lower than normal, presumably because the lesioned leg was incapable of exerting force during its stance, instead being passively dragged backwards by the forward motion of the body produced by the other stancing legs. At slower speeds, single stance motor neuron lesions occasionally produced abnormal, statically stable gaits, but slower normal gaits were also observed. Of course, lesioning all of the stance motor neurons produces no forward motion whatsoever.

Removing connections from the command neuron to the stance motor neurons of single legs had no effect at medium or high speeds, but led to statically unstable gaits at low speeds. Note that the stance reflexes of such legs are still operative and that the leg is pulled back passively as the body moves forward. Removing all of the connections from the command neuron to stance motor neurons led to statically stable, abnormal gaits. Legs would stance only briefly due to the stance reflex triggered by the forward angle sensor. Once the resulting forward motion bent the stancing legs slightly backward, the inhibition from their forward angle sensor was removed and they would swing forward again. This short swing triggered the corresponding stance reflexes and the cycle repeated. At low and medium speeds, no regular stepping pattern emerged. However, at the highest speed, a version of the tripod gait was observed (Figure 5.5).

5.3.4 Discussion

The network is extremely robust to perturbations of any individual element. The absence of a sensor, effector, or central element, or a connection between elements, does not generally lead to a complete failure of the con-

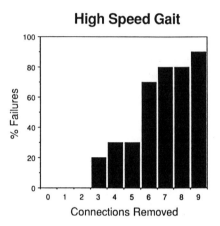

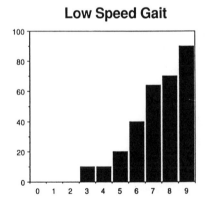
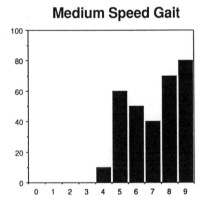

Figure 5.4: Lesions of coordinating inhibition between pacemakers. The probability of observing a statically unstable gait after the removal of from 0 to 9 coordinating inhibitory connections (out of a total of 14) is shown for the low, medium, and high speed gaits. Results shown for 7 lesions (half of the connections) represent 25 trials. All other results were obtained after 10 trials.

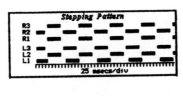

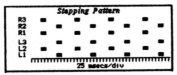

Figure 5.5: (Top) A normal tripod gait. (Bottom) After lesion of all command neuron to stance motor neuron connections.

troller. Even coordinated sets of lesions can often be tolerated. However, because the network is heterogeneous, not all perturbations are equivalent in effect.

Lesions of sensory input reveal an interesting difference between the fastest gait and the slower gaits. It appears that the tripod gait is primarily established by the central connections, because the absence of sensory input does not seriously disrupt it. On the other hand, slower gaits appear to require normal sensory input for their expression. Specifically, sensory input is crucial for the slower burst frequency of the rear pacemakers which establishes the metachronal wave.

Central lesions allow us to draw two general conclusions about the controller. First, no single central connection is essential for maintaining normal gaits at any speed. Second, they further support our observation of the difference between the tripod gait and the lower speed gaits. The tripod gait is more sensitive to random removal of coordinating inhibition than either the medium or low speed gaits, and its failure rate in response to such lesions rises more quickly. Clearly, central information is more important for the maintenance of the tripod gait than for the slower gaits.

Motor lesions, in general, were more devastating than central or sensory lesions. In particular, lesions of swing or foot motor neurons led to unstable gaits at all speeds. In effect, these lesions remove the ability of a leg to provide normal support to the body. It is well known that insects can easily adapt to the amputation of one or two legs. The poor performance

of this controller in response to leg amputations can probably be traced to
its lack of any sensory information concerning the load carried by each leg.
In insects, such information seems to play a role in adjusting the patterns of
movement of the remaining legs to compensate for missing ones (Graham,
1985).

Lesions affecting stance motor neurons have little effect on the tripod
gait, providing further evidence that it is centrally generated. The slowest
gait is most affected by these lesions. The reduced velocity of the insect
causes a loss of the entrainment which is responsible for the generation of
the metachronal wave.

Why is the controller so robust? Two explanations have been given
for the robustness of biological and artificial neural networks: redundancy
and distributed representation of information (Rumelhart and McClelland,
1986). In the purest sense, redundancy suggests multiple copies of identical subsystems, only one of which is necessary for the normal function of
the entire system. Distributed representation, on the other hand, implies
a static encoding of information throughout the network. However, the
above lesion studies suggest that neither of these concepts are the most
useful ways of understanding the robustness of the locomotion controller.
Though it is generally true that no one connection is essential for the generation of stable gaits, removing connections can have more subtle effects.
Connections that appear to be unnecessary in one gait may be crucial in
another. Furthermore, preliminary data indicate that many apparently
normal gaits are much more sensitive after lesions to small perturbations,
such as a brief push from the side. These results suggest that gaits are
not statically represented in the controller, even in a distributed sense, but
are actively constructed from the dynamic interactions between the various
components of the controller, and the insect's body and environment.

5.4   Function

Having established that the controller was quite robust to a variety of lesions, its normal operation was next analyzed in more detail. The sensory
inputs, the central elements, and their interconnections were designed to
contribute to the formation of stable gaits. What is the relative importance
of these different sources of information? This is a question which is not
only of interest for this specific controller, but is more generally relevant
to an understanding of pattern generation in biological organisms (Pear-

son, 1985). This question was investigated by isolating different parts of the controller and examining the function of these reduced networks: (1) all sensory inputs were removed; (2) all sensory inputs and motor outputs were removed; (3) the command neuron or connections from the command neuron to the pacemakers were removed; (4) the coordinating inhibition between pacemakers was removed; and (5) the ability of the pacemakers to change their interburst interval in response to external inputs was removed.

5.4.1 Removing All Sensory Inputs

The effects of removing all sensory inputs to the controller (*deafferentation*) were examined. When deafferentation was imposed after a stable gait had been established, the tripod gait was essentially unaffected, while the lower speed gaits were significantly changed. The medium speed gait became statically unstable, and the slowest gait, after a transient, became statically stable and nonmetachronal. Indeed, removing only the sensory input from the rear legs (either the forward or backward angle sensors) led to nonmetachronal gaits.

5.4.2 Removing Sensory Inputs and Motor Outputs

Removing all sensory inputs does not entirely isolate the controller from the body in which it is embedded. Whenever the insect falls down, legs that are swinging continue to move forward, while legs that are stancing cannot. As a consequence, the phase relationships between the legs will change. In some lesions which generated transient, statically unstable gaits, these periodic falls sometimes encouraged and sometimes prevented the insect from settling into a statically stable gait.

In order to determine the ability of the controller to centrally generate gaits, the pacemakers were completely isolated from the body by lesioning all sensory and motor connections. Since stepping can no longer be observed for this lesion (because the insect cannot move), the burst patterns of the pacemakers were observed instead. The activity of the pacemakers is essentially identical to the corresponding stepping patterns in the unlesioned controller (Figure 5.6, Top). The central neurons were isolated from the periphery and the pattern of pacemaker activation was examined under these conditions. If the controller was isolated from the periphery after stable gaits were established, the tripod "gait" was unaffected, but the slower "gaits" were disrupted (Figure 5.6, Bottom).

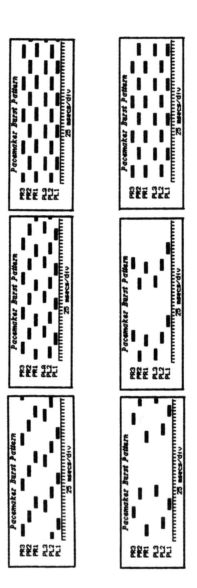

Figure 5.6: Effects of isolation on gait generation. (Top) Patterns of pace-maker activity in the normal controller during low, medium, and high speed gaits. (Bottom) Patterns of pacemaker activity after complete isolation of the locomotion controller from the body once low, medium, and high speed gaits had been established, respectively.

The slightly larger angle ranges of the rear legs are crucial to the entrainment which produces metachronal waves in the normal controller. Removal of all sensory inputs from the rear legs deprives the controller of this information. In order to determine whether metachronal waves could be generated centrally, the weight of the connections from the command neuron to the rear legs were decreased. Due to the voltage dependence of I_L, this change lowers the natural frequency of the rear pacemakers relative to the others for any given level of command neuron activation. With appropriate weights, the full range of gaits seen in the normal controller could indeed be reliably reproduced (Figure 5.7).

5.4.3   Removing the Command Neuron

Effectively lesioning the command neuron by hyperpolarizing it, and continuously pushing the insect from behind, resulted in the phenomenon of *reflex stepping*. Once a leg whose foot was down had been dragged far enough back, its backward angle sensor activated its pacemaker, causing the leg to swing forward. The forward angle sensor would then trigger the stance reflex, again putting the foot down and repeating the cycle. With appropriate forces, the full range of normal gaits was observed. Reflex stepping has also been observed in a variety of biological organisms after the removal of higher control centers (Grillner, 1981).

Removing all of the connections from the command neuron to the pacemakers before a normal gait had been established resulted in transients that were much longer than normal at all speeds. Eventually, however, the insect always fell abruptly into the correct gait for that speed. In the normal controller, it appears that the command neuron excitation sets the interburst intervals of the pacemakers close to the correct value for a given speed of walking, and that the sensory information then fine-tunes the transitions between swing and stance. In the absence of this information, the sole responsibility for the timing of these transitions falls to the sensory information. Apparently, it takes much longer to establish the proper phasing of these transitions with sensory information alone. Support for this interpretation of the role of the command neuron to pacemaker connections is also provided by earlier lesion studies, which demonstrated that removing all of the command neuron to pacemaker connections had no effect once a stable gait had already been established.

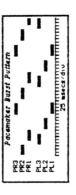

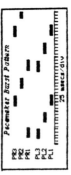

Figure 5.7: Central generation of gaits. Weights of the connections from the command neuron to the rear pacemakers were reduced 5%. The resulting burst patterns are shown for low (left), medium (middle), and high (right) levels of command neuron activation.

5.4.4 Removing Coordinating Inhibition

In the study of the robustness of the controller, the inhibitory connections between pacemakers were treated as if they were homogeneous. Here the differences between distinct subsets of these connections are considered. In order to examine the importance of coordinating information flowing from front to back, the inhibitory connections from the front to middle pacemakers, and from the middle to rear pacemakers, were removed. This lesion had no effect on slow or medium gaits, but did cause the tripod gait to become marginally statically stable. In contrast, removing the flow of information from back to front had little effect on the tripod gait, but led to abnormal, statically unstable gaits at medium speeds, and nonmetachronal, statically stable gaits at low speeds. Removing only the connections from the rear to middle pacemakers produced essentially identical results. These results, and those due to the removal of sensory input (described above), further demonstrate that coordinating inhibition from the rear pacemakers is essential to the formation of metachronal waves.

Removing all coordinating inhibitory connections across the body before a normal gait had been established led to a variety of unstable gaits, since the phase of the leg movements on each side was uncoupled. On occasion, with favorable initial conditions, insects with these lesions would walk stably. In contrast, performing this lesion on a normally walking insect had no effect at low speeds and led to normal, marginally stable gaits at higher speeds.

5.4.5 Changing Intrinsic Pacemaker Properties

The intrinsic currents provide the pacemaker neurons with their ability to produce rhythmic bursting. We have seen above that the command neuron manipulates the natural frequency of the pacemakers via the voltage dependence of I_L's duration. This contributes to the establishment of normal gaits, but does not appear to be crucial for their maintenance. What might the loss of this voltage sensitivity do to the controller? In order to investigate this question, the duration of I_L was fixed at the middle of its range (the value it would normally have for a medium speed gait). As expected, no effect on the medium speed gait was observed. At high levels of command neuron activation, an essentially normal tripod gait was also observed. However, lowering the activation level leads to a modified tripod gait. Abnormal gaits at low speeds are due to the fact that the fixed in-

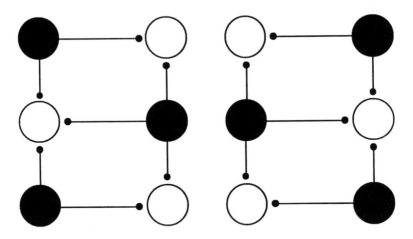

Figure 5.8: Central generation of the tripod gait. The two stable configurations of the central network during the tripod gait are shown.

terburst intervals of the pacemakers are too short for this speed, and the pacemakers are therefore initiating swings prematurely.

5.4.6   Discussion

How does this controller work? The best way to answer this question is to consider separately the high, medium, and low speed gaits. The tripod gait is the preferred solution to the constraints imposed on the pacemakers by the coordinating inhibitory connections between them (Figure 5.8). A tripod of nonadjacent pacemakers that is active receives no inhibition from the other tripod of pacemakers or from one another, and thus remain on until their high currents (I_H) shut off, or inhibition from the forward angle sensors shut them off. As a consequence, the tripod gait is primarily generated by the interactions between the central components of the controller.

Maintaining a stable pattern of activity in each tripod of pacemakers places an important timing constraint on the tripod gait, making it much less robust to certain perturbations. The swing phase of one tripod of pace-makers must not overlap that of the other tripod, or the two will attempt to turn each other off. When the insect is walking at its highest speed, the stance phases are nearly equal in duration to the swing phases. Thus, a single sensory lesion which disrupts the timing of either phase for any leg disturbs the tripod gait. In contrast, uniformly removing all sensory input, which does not disturb the relative timing of the legs, is less disruptive.

The correct duration of the interval between pacemaker bursts necessary for satisfying the timing constraints of the tripod gait is usually established by the command neuron, and can be reinforced by properly timed sensory inputs. However, if the connections from the command neuron to the pace-makers are removed, phasic sensory input can establish the tripod gait once the controller is turned on. In fact, if the network of pacemakers is excited by phasic sensory input with the correct timing, as occurs in reflex step-ping, the tripod gait will appear in the absence of any command neuron activity. Finally, sensory input from the backward angle sensor is strong enough to turn on a pacemaker even if the duration of the low current (I_L) is fixed, and so eliminating the voltage dependence of I_L's duration does not disrupt the tripod gait.

In the slowest gait, the slower burst frequency of the rear pacemakers is crucial for the establishment of metachronal waves. Clearly, the slowest gait puts significant constraints on (1) the length of the interburst intervals of the pacemakers, (2) the speed with which any leg completes its stance phase, and (3) the burst frequency of the rear pacemakers relative to that of the middle and front pacemakers. If the interburst interval is too short, the metachronal wave will not occur, because legs whose pacemakers are not receiving inhibition will begin to swing too early. This was observed when the duration of I_L was fixed at a value shorter than that seen during the slowest gait. Similarly, if the velocity of the insect was so low that its legs did not complete their stance phases before the ends of the interburst intervals of the pacemakers, legs began to swing in a nonmetachronal or-der. In addition, phasic sensory information of the correct frequency can generate the metachronal wave in the absence of the command neuron, as observed in reflex stepping.

The lower burst frequencies of the rear pacemakers relative to those of the middle and front pacemakers was due to the larger angle ranges of the rear legs. As a consequence, sensory lesions could seriously disrupt the slowest gait by changing the time for other legs to complete their stance phases, or by eliminating the phasic sensory information that slowed the burst frequency of the rear pacemakers. However, in the isolated controller, this phasic sensory information which is crucial for entrainment could be replaced by the appropriate tonic information from the command neuron (i.e., a lower level of excitation to the rear pacemakers), and still result in normal metachronal gaits.

The slowest gait was also found to be less sensitive to the random removal of connections between pacemakers than the tripod gait, as long as sufficient connections remained for entrainment to occur. The long stance phases occurring at this speed also account for the large number of abnormal but stable gaits which were observed in response to various lesions. Many nonmetachronal gaits also satisfy the constraints imposed by the coordinating inhibition while maintaining static stability.

The medium speed gait appears to combine aspects of the tripod gait with those of the slowest gait, and this combination may account for its greater robustness to many perturbations. It appears to be the least sensitive to the random removal of coordinating inhibition. This robustness is likely to be due to two factors: (1) the role of sensory input in generating the metachronal waves that characterize this gait, and (2) the less stringent timing requirements for the swing and stance phases (as compared to the tripod gait), which allows more room for adjusting the phases of the swings. However, sensory input is clearly important to the maintenance of this gait, since it fails after deafferentation. At the same time, the medium speed gait is least sensitive to single sensory lesions, perhaps because its activity pattern is stabilized to small perturbations by the coordinating inhibition between the pacemakers. Indeed, removing the central connections that allow the rear pacemakers to entrain the middle and front ones did not significantly disrupt this gait.

A longstanding debate in neurobiology has been whether patterns of activity are primarily generated centrally or peripherally (Pearson, 1985). The results of this lesion study suggest why these two hypotheses are, in general, very difficult to distinguish. Sensory feedback is clearly unnecessary in many situations. For example, when the locomotion controller is deafferented, or completely isolated from the body, it is still capable of generating many statically stable, though often abnormal, gaits. Indeed, with the appropriate weights on the connections from the command neuron to the rear pacemakers, one can observe the full range of gaits from the wave gait to the tripod gait. On the other hand, sensory information can play an important role in generating gaits. For example, reflex stepping illustrates that properly timed sensory inputs can establish normal gaits in the absence of endogenous oscillations.

Many of the central components are equally unnecessary under some conditions. For example, removing connections from the command neuron to the pacemakers does not prevent the controller from generating the full range of normal gaits. It takes longer to establish these gaits, since the coordination occurs through sensory inputs, but the command neuron to pacemaker connections are not essential for their expression. The controller can also tolerate the loss of a large fraction of inhibitory connections between pacemakers, in part because it can use sensory information to compensate for them. In addition, it is likely that incorporating sensory information about the load carried by each leg into the controller could improve its ability to tolerate the loss of an even larger proportion of central connections. Thus, the controller appears to make use of a complex interplay between sensory and central information in generating normal gaits, and the relative importance of each component differs for different speeds of walking. A similar conclusion has been reached for cockroach locomotion (Zill, 1985).

Finally, this analysis has demonstrated that embedding this neural controller in a body, even the simple body chosen here, creates additional complexities in its function. Sensory feedback reinforces and fine-tunes the centrally generated pattern. In addition, the force exerted by any one leg, acting through the body, affects the motion of all of the legs. Finally, the phase relationships between stancing and swinging legs is altered whenever the insect falls down, since swinging legs can continue to move. Thus, the resulting gaits and their stability to small perturbations are different than those produced by the disembodied controller.

It is clear that a more mathematical analysis of the dynamics of this network should be undertaken. At an abstract level, this controller can be analyzed as a collection of six coupled oscillators which are subjected to periodic forcing and damping. Questions of immediate interest include determining the set of critical parameters and the range of values for them which generate metachronal waves, and examining the stability of the resulting solutions under various conditions. However, the mathematical analysis of a heterogeneous neural network is considerably more complex than a homogeneous one. The lesion study reported here has already taught us a great deal about the dynamics of this heterogeneous neural network and can serve as a useful guide for focusing a more mathematical analysis, and interpreting its results.

Chapter 6

Exploration

6.1 Overview

Active exploration is a fundamental characteristic of living organisms. Most animals will immediately begin to explore their surroundings whenever they are placed into an unfamiliar but nonthreatening situation. Exploration is a means by which animals actively gather information about their environments. In this chapter, controllers for exploratory behavior in *P. computatrix* are presented. This is also a first step toward autonomous behavior. While the locomotion controller requires the external injection of current in order to activate it, exploration is something that the insect spontaneously does. We first consider the addition of an ability to turn. Building upon locomotion and turning, controllers for wandering, recoil, and edge-following are developed. Because no neural circuitry for any exploratory behavior is currently available, the controllers described in this chapter were designed from scratch. However, they make use of intrinsic properties and architectures which are similar in spirit to those found in natural animals.

6.2 Turning

The locomotion controller presented in Chapter 4 was designed only for straight-line walking. In order to explore, the insect must first be able to turn. There are many different ways to achieve turning. For example, with a more accurate physical model, turning could be accomplished by

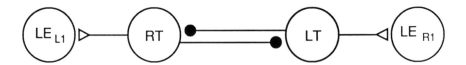

Figure 6.1: The neural circuitry underlying turning. The *LE* neurons are motor neurons controlling the lateral extensors of the front legs. These are excited by the neurons which control turning: *LT* (for left turn) and *RT* (for right turn). These neurons inhibit one another so that the insect only attempts to turn in one direction at a time.

differences in stepping frequency between the two sides of the body.

The approach chosen here emphasizes simplicity and independence of control. In straight-line locomotion, the legs apply forces which translate the body. Turning is accomplished by also allowing the front legs to also apply forces which rotate the body. When its foot is down, a front leg can cause a turn away from its side of the body by applying a lateral force. This requires the addition of one motor neuron to each front leg which controls the force of its lateral extension. As shown in Figure 6.1, these motor neurons are driven by two neurons which mutually inhibit one another so that the insect turns in only one direction at a time. These neurons are called *LT* (for Left Turn) and *RT* (for Right Turn). They form control points which abstract over the particular sensorimotor details of turning. Other neural controllers can accomplish a desired rate of turn in a given direction by exciting either *LT* or *RT* by the appropriate amount.

In this model, turning is not integrated into the locomotion system but instead serves as a perturbation to it. The locomotion system assumes that it is walking in a straight line. A turn violates this assumption, leaving the legs in slightly different configurations than it expects. The ability of the locomotion system to compensate for this perturbation is a measure of its robustness and sets an upper limit on the rate of turn using this approach. The turn rate which can be successfully accommodated depends upon the speed of walking as well as the gait utilized. This approach to turning is not perfect. The insect can fall down and it occasionally even gets its legs

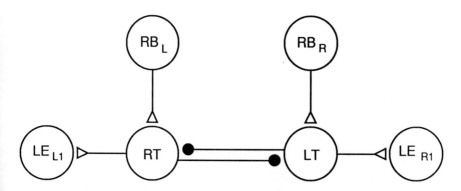

Figure 6.2: The wandering controller. The turning controller is driven by two random bursters (here labeled *RB*), which randomly excite the corresponding turn motor neurons.

so tangled that it cannot get back up. However, in practice this simple approach has proven to be quite adequate.

6.3 Wandering

Underlying any exploratory behavior is the simple ability to wander. Once the insect can turn, wandering can be easily accomplished by a circuit which randomly causes periodic turns, as shown in Figure 6.2. The turning circuit is driven by two random bursters (labeled *RB*). These cells are like pacemakers in that they contain two intrinsic currents which alternately pull the membrane potential high and low. However, unlike pacemakers, the burst and interburst durations of these two currents varies randomly. A typical path taken by *P. computatrix* as it wanders is shown in Figure 6.3. This strategy achieves reasonably good coverage of the environment and has so far proven sufficient. However, cockroaches are known to exhibit considerably more structure than this even in their seemingly random wandering. For example, *P. americana* utilizes a combination of circling and relatively straight movements in its free ranging behavior (Bell and Adiyodi, 1981, pp. 372-376). Such structured wandering could be implemented using more complex networks of coupled random bursters of the sort utilized here.

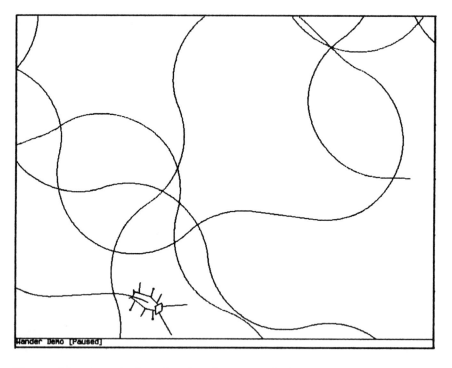

Wander Demo [Paused]

Figure 6.3: A typical path taken by a wandering insect. The walls are turned off, so that the environment wraps around like a torus. The path represents about 100 seconds of simulated time.

6.4   Recoil

In an empty environment, the above wandering controller would be sufficient to accomplish a simple form of exploration. However, such an environment would not be terribly interesting to explore. In any environment
containing other objects, the insect must be able to cope with collisions.
One possible strategy is avoidance. The insect can recoil and move away
from any contact with other objects. As discussed in the next section, this
is not the strategy employed in the final insect. However, as an example
of a nontrivial fixed-action pattern, a recoil response raises a number of
interesting issues in the design of neural controllers. It is for this reason
that the recoil controller is discussed in detail here.

A reasonable design for a recoil response is as follows. When the antennae glance off something to the side of the insect, it should briefly turn
away from the object and continue walking. On the other hand, when it
runs directly into an object, it should back up and turn before continuing
on its way. This ensures that the insect will not continue to collide with the
same object repeatedly. Relative orientations intermediate between these
two extremes should exhibit different proportions of forward and backward
walking during the recoil response. The duration of the overall response
should also be affected. A brief response is sufficient for a glancing contact,
but a head-on collision requires an extended response.

This design raises a number of issues for the recoil controller. First, it
must have some means for reversing the normal direction of walking. Second, it must be *multiphasic*, that is, it must be capable of generating both
the forward and backward phases of the response in the appropriate sequence and with the appropriate timing. Third, the controller must exhibit
orientation sensitivity. The durations of these two phases depend upon
the relative orientation between the insect and the object contacted. In
fact, if the angle of incidence is small enough, no backward walking occurs
at all. Finally, the controller must exhibit some *hysteresis*. The response
is triggered by a brief sensory stimulus, and must run to completion even
after contact has been lost. This recoil response is therefore an example of
a fixed-action pattern.

Backward walking can be implemented by a controller very similar to
that used for forward walking. The only real difference is that the roles
of the motor neurons producing the swing and stance phases must be reversed and therefore some of the connections which implement these roles
must be changed. The same controller can be used for both forward and

backward walking by including all of the connections necessary for both
and introducing a backward command neuron (*BC*) that turns on or off
connections as necessary to reverse the direction of walking. For example,
the pacemaker normally inhibits the stance motor neuron and excites the
swing motor neuron during forward walking, but this configuration must
be reversed for backward walking. This is accomplished by gating synapses
on the connections forming the combined leg controller. No changes to the
coordinating inhibitory connections are necessary. This multifunctional leg
controller is shown in Figure 6.4.

Even though this backward locomotion controller is not directly based
upon any existing neural circuitry, it makes use of the forward locomotion
circuitry in a plausible way. Many examples of such multifunctionality now
exist in the invertebrate literature (Getting and Dekin, 1985; Selverston,
1988; Kristan *et al.*, 1989). In fact, the crayfish appears to utilize the
same pattern generator for both forward and backward walking, with only
small modifications to vary the timing of muscle contractions (Kovac, 1974).
In all of these cases, circuitry is shared among a number of related but
distinct behaviors, with some mechanism for dynamically modifying the
shared circuitry into the functionally distinct configurations required for
each behavior.

By varying the level of current injected into *LC* while *BC* is active, *P.
computatrix* generates a range of backward-walking gaits which are similar
to those observed in forward walking (Figure 6.5). At high speeds of walking, the tripod gait is observed, while at slower speeds metachronal waves
appear. However, a backward walking insect exhibits *reverse* metachronal
waves, i.e. a front leg swings, then a middle leg, then a back leg. It is
not at all obvious that this should be so. Despite the fact that the rear
legs are at the leading edge of a backward-walking insect, they are still the
ones whose increased angle ranges and therefore slower step frequencies act
to establish the entrainment underlying the metachronal wave. It might
therefore be reasonably expected that metachronal waves would still travel
from the back of the insect to its front. However, this is not what is observed. Natural insects will often also exhibit reverse metachronal waves
during backward walking (Graham, 1985).

Because the recoil response consists of several phases whose duration
and very occurrence depend upon the circumstances which triggered the
response, its neural controller is considerably more interesting than that for
wandering. The recoil response controller for the right antenna is shown

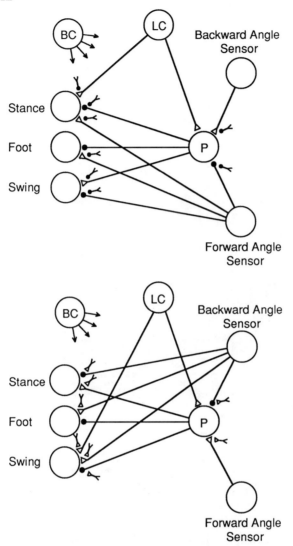

Figure 6.4: A multifunctional leg controller. (Top) In its default configuration, this circuit produces forward locomotion in the manner described in Chapter 4. (Bottom) When *BC* is activated, it reconfigures the leg controller for backward walking by gating connections. The forward locomotion connections which are disabled for backward walking are gated by inhibitory connections from *BC*. The additional connections which are enabled in order to produce backward walking are gated by excitatory connections from *BC*.

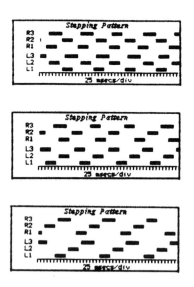

Figure 6.5: Low (bottom), medium (middle), and high (top) speed gaits observed during backward walking. Note the presence of reverse metachronal waves.

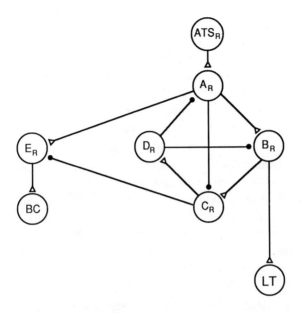

Figure 6.6: The recoil controller for the right antenna.

in Figure 6.6. The controller itself consists of the neurons ATS_R, A_R, B_R, C_R, D_R, and E_R. BC is the backward walking command neuron discussed above. LT is the left turn neuron from the turning controller. Only those connections which are actually part of the recoil controller are shown. There is another copy of this recoil response controller for the left antenna.

The antenna tactile sensor (ATS_R) generates a burst whose frequency is proportional to the relative orientation of the body and the tangent line of the object at the point of contact; the larger the angle, the higher the firing frequency. A head-on collision produces a high frequency burst and a glancing contact produces a low frequency one. This burst excites A_R, which is a *trigger cell*. Neuron A_R translates a brief burst of activity into an extended response whose characteristics depend upon those of the initial burst. Whenever external currents cause it to burst, an intrinsic current is triggered whose magnitude and duration is proportional to the membrane potential of the cell. This cell governs the duration of the entire recoil response. The other neurons B_R, C_R, and D_R control the durations of the various phases of the response and have large time constants (on the order of tens to hundreds of milliseconds) and high thresholds.[1]

---

[1] As illustrated here, either intrinsic currents or a large capacitance may be used to

This controller operates as follows. When the right antenna contacts an object, ATS_R generates a brief burst whose frequency is proportional to the contact angle. This brief burst produces an extended burst in the trigger neuron A_R whose frequency and duration are proportional to the activity of ATS_R. Activity in A_R excites E_R. If E_R goes above threshold, then it causes the insect to walk backward by exciting BC. Thus E_R implements the decision whether or not to back up based upon the contact angle.

In addition, A_R excites B_R. After an initial delay due to its slightly larger time constant, B_R will begin to burst and cause a turn to the left by exciting LT. After a somewhat longer delay, B_R will cause C_R to burst, shutting off E_R. This removes any excitation that E_R may have been providing to BC, and allows the insect to continue walking forward. The time it takes C_R to go above threshold is also modulated by the inhibitory connection from A_R. The effect of this connection is to increase the delay before C_R bursts as a function of the activity of A_R. Therefore, the more head-on a collision is, the more backing up the insect will do.

C_R also excites D_R. After another delay, during which the insect is walking forward and still turning away from the contacted object, D_R will burst, inhibiting A_R and B_R and thus terminating the recoil response. For glancing contacts, the trigger current in A_R can terminate before the A_R, B_R, C_R, D_R loop completes. In this case, only a short turn away from the direction of contact with the object is generated. The response of an insect containing this controller is shown for three different angles of incidence in Figure 6.7. It is interesting to note that the angle with which the insect leaves an obstacle is largely independent of its angle of incidence. This exit angle appears to be an invariant of the dynamics of the recoil controller.

This controller is complex and the above description has only been able to give the overall flavor of its operation. This controller is certainly not the only way to implement this behavior. However, this particular design has the advantage that the timing of the various phases of the response can be manipulated by biasing the cells in the loop or modulating their interconnections. In any case, this section has shown how neural controllers for behaviors with fairly complex temporal characteristics can be implemented.

---

endow a model neuron with an extended response. Each of these techniques has its advantages and disadvantages and both will be employed throughout this book. For example, giving a model neuron a large capacitance is simple, but it slows that cell's response to any change. On the other hand, defining intrinsic currents is more difficult, but their effects can be made more selective.

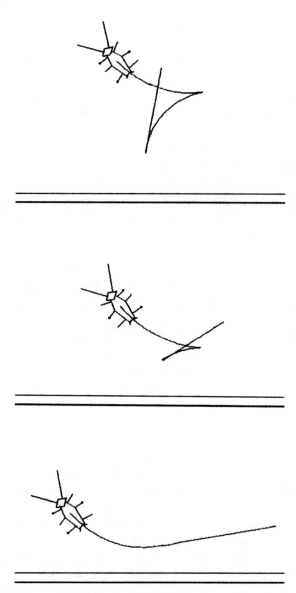

Figure 6.7: The recoil responses generated by the recoil controller for three different angles of incidence. (Bottom) A small angle of incidence produces only a turn away from the wall. (Middle) A larger angle of incidence results in a small amount of backing up as the insect turns away. (Top) A nearly head-on collision results in a great deal of backing up and turning away.

6.5   Edge-Following

Another strategy for handling contacts with other objects is to follow rather
than recoil from them. In this approach, an insect attempts to orient its
body parallel to any object it encounters and follow its edge. This strategy
appears to be better suited to the traversal of complex environments than
is recoil. It is also somewhat more biologically realistic. Cockroaches in
particular are known to spend a majority of their time within antennal
contact of an edge (Bell and Adiyodi, 1981, p. 373).

The key problem for edge-following is achieving and maintaining a
nearly parallel orientation between the insect's body and the edge it is
following. If the angle between the insect and the edge it is following is too
large, the insect must turn away from the edge in order to decrease this angle. If, on the other hand, this angle is too small, then the insect must turn
toward the edge in order to increase it. This behavior must also exhibit
some hysteresis. Once the insect is following an edge, it should continue
to do so even if contact is occasionally lost (i.e., like the recoil response,
edge-following should exhibit some behavioral hysteresis). However, the
behavior should not continue indefinitely after contact has been lost.

The edge-following controller for the right antenna is shown in Figure 6.8. A similar circuit governs edge-following on the left side of the
body. The right edge-following controller operates as follows. When an
object is contacted, the antenna tactile sensor (ATS_R) generates a burst
whose frequency is proportional to the angle between the body and the
edge at the point of contact. A head-on collision produces a high frequency
burst and a glancing contact produces a low frequency one. This response
is identical to that in the recoil controller. However, here these sensors
have different intrinsic properties than they did in the recoil controller. An
antenna tactile sensor in the edge-following controller is similar to a trigger cell in some respects. It can translate a brief contact into an extended
response. Thus, it is capable of "holding" the relative orientation between
the insect and the edge at the last contact for a short period of time.

ATS_R excites Q_R, a neuron whose capacitance is large enough to smooth
the insect's response to discontinuities in the edge it is following. Activity
in QR has a number of effects. First, it excites F_R. This neuron has a low
threshold, high gain, and large capacitance. F_R is therefore easily saturated
and it maintains its saturation for some period of time after excitation is
removed. It implements the hysteresis of the edge-following behavior.

Q_R also connects to L_R and H_R. Together, these neurons act to main-

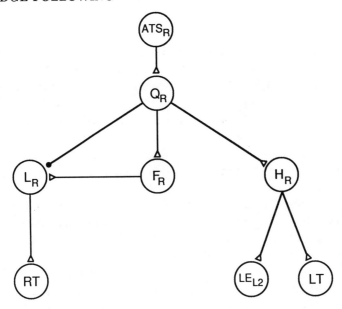

Figure 6.8: The right edge-following controller.

tain a nearly parallel orientation between the insect's body and the edge it is following. H_R acts to decrease the angle between the body and the edge when it is too large (H_R is active when the angle is too <u>H</u>igh) and L_R acts to increase this angle when it is too small (L_R is active when the angle is too <u>L</u>ow). The operation of these neurons is explained in more detail below.

When the insect is following an edge to its right at too large an angle, H_R causes a left turn away from the edge in order to decrease the relative angle between them. The magnitude of the turn it generates is proportional to the size of the deviation. H_R's threshold and the excitation it receives from QR are set such that H_R only fires when the angle is greater than the proper orientation.

For a given speed of walking, there is a limit to how fast the insect can orient to a new edge. In order to orient as quickly as possible, we would like the turn generated by H_R to be as large as possible. However, too large a turn will leave the insect out of contact with the edge long enough for edge-following to cease. In order to decrease the time the right antenna is out of contact, the right edge-following controller utilizes the lateral extensor in the middle left leg to slide the body toward the edge as it turns away from it.

If the angle between the insect's body and the edge it is following becomes too small, L_R is triggered. This neuron causes a right turn toward the edge the insect was following in order to increase the relative angle between them. Because this neuron is also active when it receives no excitation from Q_R while F_R is active (i.e. when contact with an edge which was being followed is lost) it is also important for restoring contact with an edge. The strengths of the inhibition and excitation L_R receives are set such that this neuron only fires when the angle is less than the desired orientation.

The operation of the right edge-following controller can be summarized as follows. Whenever an edge is contacted on the right side of the body, F_R is triggered and L_R and H_R act to orient the body along it. As the insect follows the edge, L_R and H_R continue to keep it properly oriented by generating turns either toward or away from the edge as necessary. If contact with the edge is lost, L_R tries to reestablish contact. If contact is not reestablished before activity in F_R ceases, then the edge-following behavior terminates. The path of an insect following a curving wall is shown in Figure 6.9.

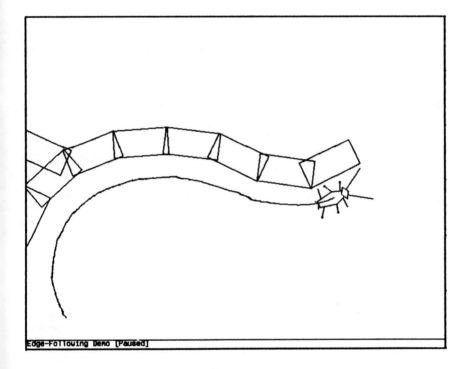

Figure 6.9: The path of an insect following a wall.

Chapter 7

Feeding

7.1 Introduction

A crucial behavior for any natural organism is feeding. Each of its actions consumes energy and its limited supply must repeatedly be replenished or the organism will die. Similarly, each action of *P. computatrix* has an associated energy cost. If an insect's energy supply is exhausted, it is removed from the environment. Therefore, as its energy diminishes, the insect must actively seek out and consume food. Feeding is the first example of a goal-oriented behavior in *P. computatrix*. It is also a significant step toward autonomous behavior, moving away from the externally-triggered reflexes and fixed-action patterns of the previous chapter to a behavior which is internally initiated and maintained. Another important aspect of feeding is that the insect's performance is externally evaluated by the environment. Its ability to feed when necessary actually matters to its survival in a way that the previous behaviors did not.

7.2 Feeding as a Motivated Behavior

While an animal's external environment certainly plays an extremely important role in shaping its actions, the behavior of even simpler animals is by no means solely reactive. The response of an animal to food, for example, cannot be explained only in terms of the physical stimuli involved. On two different occasions, the very same animal may behave in completely different ways when presented with seemingly identical pieces of food (e.g. hungrily consuming it in one case and ignoring or even avoiding it in another). To account for these differences, behavioral scientists hypothesize internal motivational states or drives which modulate an animal's response to its environment. These internal factors play a particularly important role in complex behavior, but are present to some degree in nearly all animal behavior. Behaviors which exhibit an extensive dependence on motivational variables are termed *motivated behaviors*.

While a rigorous definition is difficult to state, behaviors spoken of as motivated generally exhibit some subset of the following six characteristics (Kupfermann, 1974):

1. Grouping and sequencing of behavior in time. Behaviors spoken of as motivated typically involve preparatory or *appetitive behaviors* that serve to orient the organism to a goal object, followed by final *consummatory behaviors* that directly serve to obtain the goal object. Sequencing implies the operation of internal mechanisms that insure the proper timing and intensity of the behavior.

2. Directedness. Behavior is directed in the sense that organisms utilize any one of a variety of motor patterns to achieve a goal condition. The sequence of different response patterns shown by a behaving animal often can be understood only by reference to some goal.

3. Spontaneity of behavior. Behaviors can occur in the absence of any recognizable eliciting stimuli.

4. Changes in responsiveness due to a presumed change in internal state, such as satiation in a hungry animal. Changes in responsiveness can also be due to learning. Changes due to learning typically are long-lasting and are the result of patterns of external sensory stimulation. Changes due to alterations in motivational states typically are short-lasting and cyclical, and can be best understood as arising from changes in body chemistry or internal sensory stimulation.

5. Persistence of behavior which can greatly outlast the initiating stimulus, e.g. arousal following a strong or significant stimulus. Some nonassociative behavioral changes such as arousal or sensitization represent a convergence of the concepts of motivation and learning. Like

motivational states, arousal is typically short-lasting, but, like learning, arousal is an adaptive change of behavior in response to external
sensory stimuli.

6. Occurrence of associative learning. Since the occurrence of learning is
   often dependent upon a given motivational state such as hunger, the
   existence of associative learning has sometimes been used as evidence
   for the operation of a motivational state.

Motivational states are pervasive in mammalian behavior. However,
they have also proven to be essential for explaining the behavior of simpler
animals as well. Unfortunately, the explanatory utility of these internal
factors is limited by the fact that they are hypothetical constructs, inferred
by the theorist to intervene between stimulus and action in order to account
for otherwise inexplicable responses. What might be the neural basis of
these motivational states?

The neural implementation of a feeding behavior for *P. computatrix*
can begin to address this question. Feeding is a prototypical motivated
behavior in which attainment of the goal object (food) is clearly crucial to
an animal's survival. In this case, the relevant motivational state is hunger.
When an animal is hungry, it will exhibit a sequence of *appetitive behaviors*
which serve to identify and properly orient the animal to food. Once food is
available, *consummatory behaviors* are generated to ingest it. On the other
hand, a satiated animal may ignore or even avoid sensory stimuli which
suggest the presence of food (Kupfermann, 1974).

7.3 Appetitive Component

The appetitive component of feeding is responsible for getting a hungry insect to a food patch. This behavior is an example of a taxis. To accomplish
the required orientation, the appetitive controller utilizes the locomotion,
wandering, and edge-following capabilities of the insect. The interactions
between the neural circuitry underlying these behaviors and the feeding
controller presented in this chapter are described in chapter 8. Assuming
that the insect is already close enough to a food patch that the chemical
sensors in its antennae can detect an odor signal, there are two separate
issues which must be addressed by this phase of the behavior. First, the
insect must use the information from the chemical sensors in its antennae
to turn itself toward the food patch as it walks. Second, this orientation

should only occur when the insect is actually in need of energy. Correspondingly, the appetitive neural controller (Figure 7.1) consists of two distinct components.

The orientation component is comprised of the upper six neurons in Figure 7.1. Chemical sensors in each antennae (ACS) are used to detect the presence of a chemical signal. These sensors have a large but limited dynamic range. Because of the $1/d^2$ diffusion law, they will be unable to detect any odor from too great a distance and will saturate very near a food source.

The odor signals detected by the chemical sensors in each antenna (ACS) are compared (by LOS and ROS), and the difference between them is used to generate a turn toward the stronger side. This computation is performed essentially by subtraction: an ACS (antenna chemical sensor) excites the relative odor strength neuron on its side of the body and inhibits the one on the opposite side. In order to be effective for small signals, these gradient detection neurons have large gains. The turn is accomplished by exciting the corresponding turn interneuron (LT or RT) by an amount proportional to the size of the difference.

The second component is responsible for controlling whether or not the insect actually orients to a nearby patch of food. This decision depends upon its internal energy level, and is controlled by the bottom three neurons in Figure 7.1. The current energy level of the insect is monitored by an internal energy sensor (ES). Though the odor gradient is continuously being sensed by the odor strength neurons (LOS and ROS), their connections to the turn interneurons (LT and RT) are normally disabled, preventing access of this information to the motor apparatus which turns the insect. As the insect's energy level falls, however, so does the activity of its energy sensor (ES). This decreasing activity gradually releases the spontaneously active feeding arousal neuron (FA) from inhibition. When activity in FA becomes sufficient to fire the search command neuron (SC), the connections between the odor strength neurons and the turn neurons are enabled by gating connections from SC, and the insect begins to orient to food.

7.4   Consummatory Component

Once the appetitive controller has successfully oriented the insect to food, the consummatory component of the behavior is triggered. This fixed-

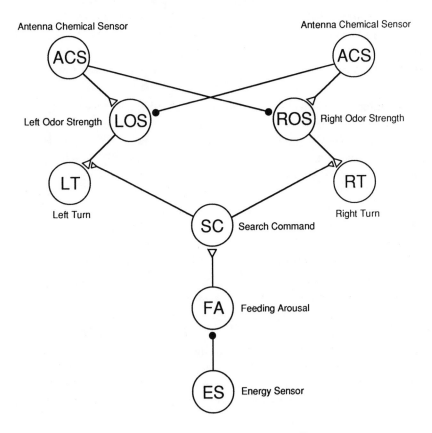

Figure 7.1: The appetitive controller.

action pattern consists of rhythmic biting movements which persist until sufficient food has been ingested. Like the appetitive phase, consummatory behavior should only be released when the insect is in need of energy.

An animal's interest in feeding (its *feeding arousal*), may be a function of more than just its energy requirements. Other factors, such as the exposure of an animal to the taste, odor, or tactile sensations of food, can significantly increase its feeding arousal. This relationship between feeding and arousal, in which the very act of feeding further enhances an animal's interest in feeding, leads to a form of behavioral hysteresis. Once food is encountered, an animal may feed well beyond the internal energy requirements which initiated the behavior. In many animals, this hysteresis is thought to play a role in the patterning of feeding behavior into discrete meals rather than continuous grazing (Susswein, Weiss, and Kupfermann, 1978). At some point, of course, the ingested food must be capable of overriding the arousing effects of consummatory behavior, or the animal would never cease to feed.

The neural controller for the consummatory phase of feeding is shown in Figure 7.2. Tactile (MTS) and chemical (MCS) sensors in the mouth are used to detect the presence of food. MCS is considerably less sensitive than the chemical sensors in the antennae, so it can only detect the odor from food which is very close to the mouth. Both of these sensors excite the food present (FP) neuron. The threshold of FP is set so that it will fire only when there is sufficient activity in both MTS and MCS. The conjunction of tactile and chemical signals is required in order to prevent attempts to ingest nonfood patches and, due to the diffusion of odors, to prevent biting from beginning before the food patch is actually reached.

Activity in FP excites the consummatory command neuron (CC). If this excitation is coupled with sufficient excitation from FA (i.e. if the insect is sufficiently aroused to feeding), then CC fires and ingestion begins. Because the threshold of the consummatory command neuron is somewhat lower than that of the search command neuron (SC), an insect which is not sufficiently aroused to orient to food may nevertheless consume food that is directly presented to its mouth. CC excites the bite pacemaker (BP) to generate rhythmic bursts which cause a motor neuron (MO) to open and close the mouth.

The motor neuron controlling the mouth (MO) also makes an excitatory connection onto the feeding arousal neuron (FA), which in turn makes an excitatory modulatory synapse onto the connection between the consum-

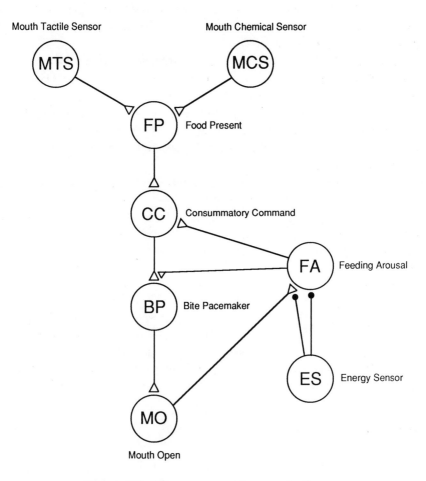

Figure 7.2: The consummatory controller.

matory command neuron (CC) and the bite pacemaker (BP). The net effect of these excitatory connections is a positive feedback loop. Corresponding to each bite is a burst of activity in MO. This burst excites FA, which in turn increases the effect of CC on BP via a modulatory synapse on the connection between them. Like the pacemakers in the locomotion controller, BP's interburst interval is sensitive to the level of external excitation or inhibition it receives. Increasing the gain of this connection therefore increases the level of excitation that BP receives from CC, which in turn makes BP (and thus MO) burst more frequently. Due to the large capacitance of FA, these bursts are temporally summed, resulting in a higher average activity of FA.

Thus activity in FA increases the bite frequency and a higher bite frequency further excites FA, until its firing frequency saturates. This positive feedback loop ensures that FA remains active during biting beyond the point at which it receives enough inhibition from ES to normally silence it. This neural positive feedback loop is inspired by work on the neural basis of feeding arousal maintenance in *Aplysia* (Weiss, Chiel, Koch, and Kupfermann, 1986).

Of course, this positive feedback loop must eventually be broken, or the insect will remain in the consummatory phase indefinitely. As the insect consumes food, its energy level begins to rise. This leads to increased activity in ES which both directly inhibits FA, and also decreases the gain of the positive feedback loop via an inhibitory modulatory synapse onto the connection between MO and FA. At some point, these inhibitory effects will overcome the positive feedback and activity in FA will drop low enough to terminate the feeding behavior. The capacitance of these cells and the weights of their interconnections, as well as the intrinsic current characteristics of BP, can be set so that satiation occurs when the energy store of the insect is approximately full. This neural mechanism is based upon a similar one hypothesized to underlie satiation in *Aplysia* (Weiss, Chiel, and Kupfermann, 1986).

7.5   Results

A typical path produced by the appetitive controller as it guides an insect toward food is shown in Figure 7.3. As can be seen, this controller does a reasonably good job of orienting the insect to food. However, two difficulties with this controller have been observed. While neither of these problems

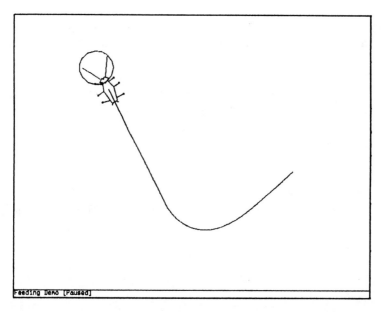

Feeding Demo [Paused]

Figure 7.3: The path of an insect orienting to a food patch by following the odor gradient.

have proven to be very severe, they are mentioned here as possible directions for future improvement. First of all, this controller often causes the insect to wave its body back and forth near food. This oscillations are due to the large gains in this controller. While these gains are necessary for the operation of this controller at great distances from food, they are too large for the signal intensities that occur near food. There are several possible ways to eliminate these oscillations. For example, some form of adaptive gain control could be used, or multiple sensors with different dynamic ranges could be employed. In practice, these oscillations have never interfered with an insect's ability to orient to food.

A second problem is caused by the limited turn radius of the insect coupled with the simple orientation strategy employed. For certain orientations and distances, these sometimes combine to cause the insect to "orbit" around a food patch rather than actually reaching it. This problem is rare, but more devastating than the above oscillations when it occurs. This could be avoided either by adopting a turning strategy which allowed a smaller turn radius than is currently possible, or by using backward walking when the signal is very strong and the gradient large.

The feeding behavior of *P. computatrix* has been found to exhibit four
of the six characteristics of motivated behavior which were described in
Section 7.2:

1. **Grouping and sequencing of behavior in time**. When the artificial insect is "hungry", it generates appetitive and consummatory
   behaviors with the proper sequence, timing, and intensity in order to
   obtain food. The insect's ability to assemble appropriate sequences
   of behavior will be the focus of the next chapter.

2. **Goal-Directedness**. Regardless of its environmental situation, a
   hungry insect will generate movements which serve to obtain food.
   Therefore, the behavior of a hungry insect can only be understood by
   reference to an internal goal. Due to the internal effects of the energy
   sensor (ES) and feeding arousal (FA) neurons on the controllers, the
   insect's external stimuli are insufficient to account for its behavior.

3. **Changes in responsiveness due to a change in internal state**.
   While a hungry insect will attempt to orient to and consume any
   nearby food, a satiated one will ignore it (Figure 7.4). In addition,
   once a hungry insect has consumed sufficient food, it will simply walk
   over the food patch which initially attracted it.

4. **Persistence**. If a hungry insect is removed from food before it has
   fed to satiation, its feeding arousal will persist, and it will continue
   to exhibit feeding movements.

How can the artificial insect's feeding arousal be characterized behaviorally? One technique that has been applied to the study of feeding arousal
in natural animals is the examination of the time interval between successive bites as an animal feeds under various conditions. In *Aplysia*, for
example, the interbite interval progressively decreases as an animal begins
to feed (showing a build-up of arousal), and increases as the animal satiates. In addition, the rate of rise and fall of arousal depends upon the
initial degree of satiation (Susswein, Weiss, and Kupfermann, 1978). These
characteristics are illustrated in Figure 7.5.

In order to examine the role of feeding arousal in the artificial insect,
we performed a similar set of experiments. Food was directly presented
to insects with differing degrees of initial satiation, and the time interval
between successive bites was recorded for the entire resulting consummatory

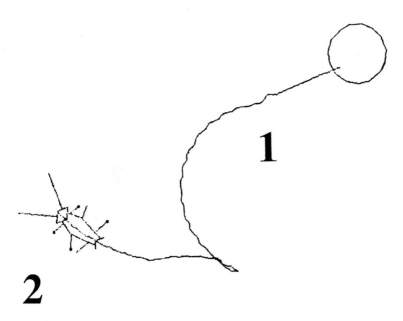

Figure 7.4: The insect's internal state affects its responsiveness to food. (1) A hungry insect orients and locomotes to food. (2) A satiated insect placed into an identical environmental situation ignores the food patch and wanders away.

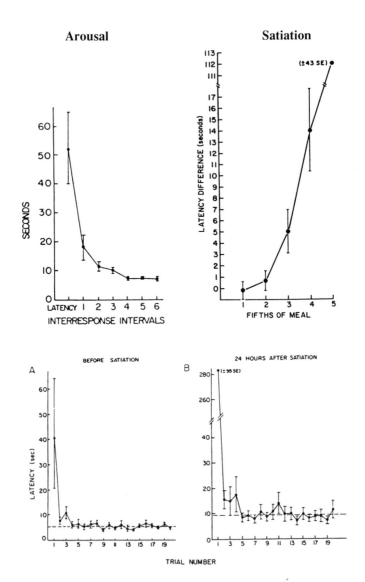

Figure 7.5: Arousal and Satiation in *Aplysia*. (Top Left) Build-up of arousal. (Top Right) Decay of arousal. (Bottom) Effects of satiation on build-up of arousal. (Reprinted with permission from *The effects of food arousal on the latency of biting in* Aplysia, by A.J. Susswein, K.R. Weiss, and I. Kupferman, *J. Comp. Physiol.* **123**:31-41. Copyright ©1978 Springer-Verlag.)

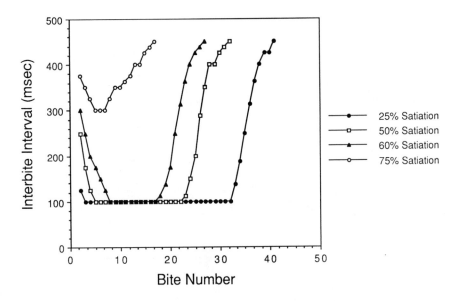

Figure 7.6: Build-up of arousal and satiation in *P. computatrix* for different initial levels of satiation.

response. Above an energy level of approximately 80% of capacity, insects could not be induced to bite. Below this level, however, insects began to consume the food. As these insects fed, the interbite interval decreased as their feeding arousal built up until some minimum interval was achieved (Figure 7.6). The rate of build-up of arousal was slowest for those insects with the highest initial degree of satiation. In fact, an insect whose energy level was already 75% of capacity never achieved full arousal. As the feeding insects neared satiation, their interbite interval increased as arousal waned. The rate of fall-off of arousal was essentially identical for all insects in which full arousal was achieved. It is interesting to note that, regardless of the initial degree of satiation, all insects in which biting was triggered fed until their energy stores were approximately 99% full. The appropriate number of bites to achieve this were generated in all cases. These results suggest that the neural mechanisms which have been proposed to underlie feeding arousal and satiation in *Aplysia* are capable of producing interbite interval graphs which are at least qualitatively similar to those that have actually been observed.

What is the neural basis of these arousal and satiation phenomena?

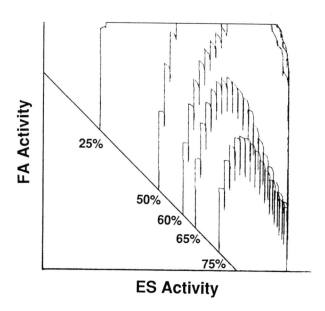

Figure 7.7: Phase plot of FA vs. ES activity for a variety of initial degrees of satiation.

Clearly, the answer lies in the interactions between the internal energy sensor and the positive feedback loop mediated by the feeding arousal neuron, but the precise nature of the interaction is not at all clear from the qualitative descriptions of the neural controllers given earlier. In order to more carefully examine this interaction, a phase plot of the activity in these two neurons under the experimental conditions described above was produced (Figure 7.7).

An insect with a full complement of energy begins at the lower right-hand corner of the diagram, with maximum activity in ES and no activity in FA. As the insect's energy begins to fall, it moves to the left on the ES axis until the inhibition from ES is insufficient to hold FA below threshold. At this point, activity in FA begins to increase. Since the positive feedback loop is not yet active because no biting has occurred, a linear decrease in energy results in a linear increase in FA activity. If no food is consumed, the insect continues to move along this line toward the upper left of the diagram until its energy is exhausted.

If biting is triggered by the presence of food at the mouth, the relationship between FA and ES changes drastically. As the insect begins consuming food, activity in FA initially increases as arousal builds up, and then later decreases as the insect satiates. Each "bump" corresponds to the arousing effects on FA of one bite via the positive feedback loop and to the small increase of energy from the food consumed in that bite. Trajectories are shown for energy levels of 25%, 50%, 60%, 65%, and 75% of capacity.

The precise shape of these trajectories depend greatly upon the initial levels of activity in FA and ES when the consummatory response is triggered. In an insect with a relatively low energy level (i.e. 25% of capacity) FA activity saturates in two bites. This can be explained by the fact that the inhibition provided by ES is fairly low in this case, allowing a large gain on the positive feedback connection from MO to FA. For higher levels of energy, the inhibition from ES lowers this loop gain, requiring many more bites before FA saturates. In all cases, these trajectories are highly non-linear, because the activity of ES, and thus the strength of the inhibition it provides, changes throughout the feeding response as food is consumed.

These differences in rise to saturation account for the observed differences between the initial segments of the interbite interval curves in Figure 7.6. In addition, note that for all trajectories which saturate FA, the fall-off of activity in FA as full ES activity is reached (i.e. as the energy level nears 100%) is essentially identical. This explains why the latter portions of the 25%, 50%, and 60% interbite interval curves in Figure 7.6 are so similar, despite the fact that their initial segments are rather different.

Initial energy levels greater than somewhere between 60% and 65% of capacity result in trajectories which never saturate FA. Under these conditions, the inhibition from ES is very strong, keeping the gain of the positive feedback loop sufficiently small to prevent saturation. It can also be seen that the fall-off of FA activity is much slower than for those trajectories which saturate FA. These observations explain the distinctive shape of the 75% interbite interval curve in Figure 7.6. Finally, initial energy levels greater than approximately 80% fail to initiate biting because the corresponding activity in FA is insufficient to trigger the consummatory command neuron (CC).

Internal factors can significantly impact an animal's responses to its environment. From the perspective of an external observer, the concept of motivational states have played an important role in explaining these effects. But what is the actual neural basis of these motivational states? Given the above results, we must conclude that there is no simple neural correlate to the artificial insect's "desire" for food. Indeed, the so-called feeding arousal neuron appears to be something of a misnomer. From a neural perspective, the insect's response to food is the result of a complex dynamics of interaction between an internal positive feedback loop (mediated by FA) and a negative feedback loop (mediated by ES) which is closed through the external environment. Of course, the artificial insect is only a very simple "animal." These results illustrate the difficulty of relating behaviorally relevant distinctions drawn by an external observer to the internal neural processes which generate them.

Chapter 8

Behavioral Choice

8.1 Introduction

The world is not a static place. The weather and terrain change, energy stores are depleted and replenished, and potential mates and predators appear and disappear. In order to survive, an animal must constantly decide what to do next. These decisions may take the form of minor adjustments to an ongoing behavior (i.e. changes in gait) or switches between two discrete behaviors (i.e. from feeding to escape).

Previous chapters have been primarily concerned with the design of neural controllers for a variety of individual behaviors which are important to *P. computatrix* in coping with its environment. Many of these controllers include mechanisms for adjusting their responses to changing internal and external conditions. However, while some of these controllers implicitly depended upon the existence of others (e.g. several controllers utilized the turning controller and most of them assumed the existence of the locomotion controller), the interactions between controllers for different behaviors have largely been ignored.

This strategy considerably simplified the presentation of these individual controllers. Because they share the same motor apparatus, however, many of the insect's behaviors are potentially incompatible. For example, the wandering, edge-following, and appetitive controllers all utilize the lateral extensors of the front legs to turn the insect, often in different directions. In addition, while locomotion is crucial to these three behaviors, locomotion

141

during the consummatory response would be disastrous. Properly managing the interactions between its various behaviors is extremely important to the behavioral cohesiveness of the insect as it confronts its environment. The ability to switch appropriately between different behaviors in the face of changing internal and external conditions is certainly a crucial component of natural animal behavior. How should the artificial insect's nervous system be organized so that the many individual neural controllers always generate globally coherent behavior? This chapter explicitly addresses the neural implementation of such behavioral interactions.

8.2   Behavioral Organization of *P. computatrix*

Before embarking upon a detailed examination of the underlying neural mechanisms, we should first consider the desired behavioral interactions. The behavioral repertoire of *P. computatrix* consists of four major components: the appetitive phase of feeding, the consummatory phase of feeding, edge-following, and wandering.[1] Generally speaking, feeding should take precedence over edge-following, which in turn should take precedence over wandering. These behaviors can therefore be organized into the behavioral hierarchy shown in Figure 8.1.

In this diagram, each major behavior is represented by an ellipse. Locomotion is not explicitly represented as a separate behavior, since it is implicitly utilized by most of the other behaviors. In addition, certain other important interactions, such as that between the edge-following controllers on each side of the body (crucial in corners), are not explicitly represented in this diagram. Sensory stimuli which play a role in triggering a given behavior are shown as rectangular boxes, while the motivational state governing feeding is represented by a diamond. The interactions between these various components are illustrated by excitatory and inhibitory connections. This diagram roughly corresponds to that which an Ethologist might construct to describe the interrelationships between the various behaviors of a natural animal.

In general, whenever a higher order behavior is triggered, it suppresses lower order behaviors. Note, however, that the diagram in Figure 8.1 is not strictly hierarchical. While feeding normally takes precedence over edge-

---

[1] Recall from Chapter 6 that the recoil response was not incorporated into the final insect. This recoil controller actually already included a mechanism for behavioral choice: choosing between forward and backward walking.

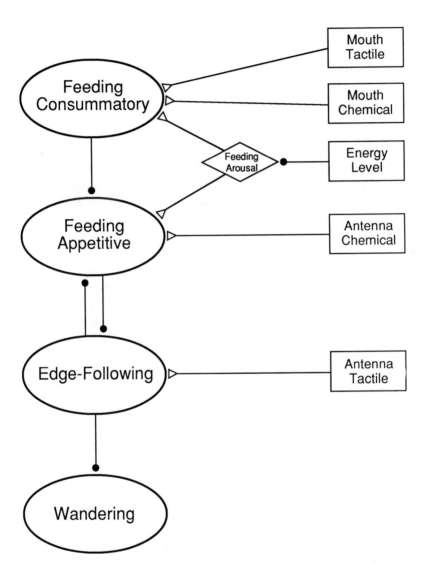

Figure 8.1: The behavioral organization of *P. computatrix*. Behaviors are shown as ellipses, boxes represent sensory stimuli, and the motivational state governing feeding is shown as a diamond. The interrelationships between these various components are illustrated with excitatory and inhibitory connections. This diagram is not strictly hierarchical. The two-way connection between edge-following and the appetitive phase of feeding illustrates the context dependence of their relationship.

following, this precedence should reverse if an obstacle blocks the insect's path to food. In this case, the insect should follow the edge of the obstacle in the hope of getting around it. The relationship between these two behaviors is therefore dependent upon the environmental context.

8.3   Neural Mechanisms for Behavioral Choice

The excitatory and inhibitory connections in Figure 8.1 are meant only to illustrate the interactions between the artificial insect's various behaviors. How can these interactions be implemented neurally? From the few instances of behavioral choice whose neuronal basis has been studied, there seems to be no single answer to this question. A variety of mechanisms are employed (Kristan *et al.*, 1989). In some cases, behavioral choice appears to be mediated by inhibition between the pattern generators for each behavior, e.g. the choice between walking and flight in the locust (Ramirez and Pearson, 1988). In other cases, such as the choice between forward and backward walking in crayfish (Kovac, 1974), the expression of a given pattern generator is varied in order to produce different behaviors. Finally, portions of the same pattern generator may be functionally rewired for different behaviors, e.g. the choice between withdrawal and swimming in the sea slug *Tritonia* in response to a tactile stimulus (Getting and Dekin, 1985). Animals may in fact use combinations of all three mechanisms.

Indeed, Altman and Kien (1987; 1989) have argued that behavioral choice is not governed by discrete command centers which simply switch between different pattern generators as appropriate. Rather, they suggest that decisions are made in a highly distributed fashion, by consensus among multiple centers potentially involving much of the nervous system. On their view, the actual behavior expressed by an animal at any given point in time is actively constructed from the sum total of interactions among many interneuronal feedback loops, external sensory inputs, and internal physiological state. This "holistic" view of behavioral choice seems more in keeping with the range and flexibility of behavior actually observed in natural animals. However, its elucidation would require a detailed understanding of neural circuitry on a larger scale than is currently possible.

The neural basis of behavioral choice in *P. computatrix* is similar in spirit to the above observed and hypothesized neurobiological mechanisms. Decisions are made by consensus among the individual controllers rather than by a centralized command center. However, these interactions are much simpler than those envisioned by Altman and Kien. In most cases, the required interactions between two behaviors can be directly implemented by explicit connections between the corresponding command neurons. For example, edge-following behavior can suppress wandering via direct inhibitory connections from a key neuron in each of the edge-following controllers to a key neuron in the wandering controller.

The neural implementation of other interactions is more complex. The edge-following and appetitive controllers are particularly interesting in this regard. Neither of these controllers can simply suppress the other because situations exist in which either one should dominate. The neural implementation of this relationship therefore requires additional circuitry which modifies the interaction between these two controllers depending upon the environmental context.

8.4 Locomotion Controller Revisions

As described in Chapter 4, the locomotion controller makes use of a single command neuron LC for controlling the speed of walking. This neuron was given a large capacitance in order to spread gait changes over several steps and thus ensure the stability of the metachronal wave. However, there are situations where other controllers may need to abruptly start or stop walking. For example, once the appetitive controller has positioned food beneath the mouth, locomotion should cease almost immediately or the food will be passed over.

In order to support the ability to quickly stop or start locomotion, the original locomotion command neuron LC was divided into two neurons called LCS and LCF. The new leg controller is shown in Figure 8.2. LCS has the same capabilities as LC. It has a large capacitance and is used primarily for slow gait and speed changes. LCF is interposed between LCS and the remainder of the leg controller. It has a small capacitance and unity gain. Normally, therefore, LCF simply passes through LCS's current activity. However, other controllers can quickly affect the speed of walking by manipulating LCF. For example, the walking can be suddenly stopped by strongly inhibiting LCF, even though LCS is still active.

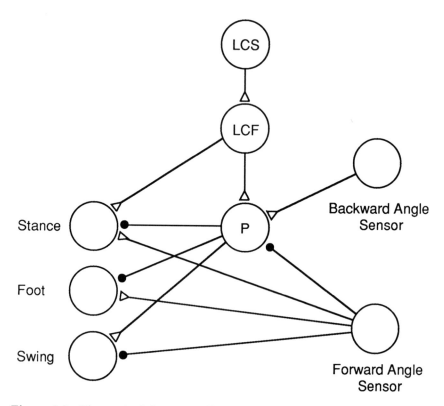

Figure 8.2: The revised leg controller. The original locomotion command neuron LC has been divided into two neurons. LCS can be used to slowly change the speed of walking and thus ensure continuous stability of the metachronal wave. When necessary, LCF can be directly manipulated for more abrupt changes in speed, such as a sudden stop.

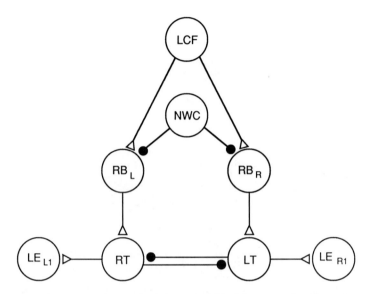

Figure 8.3: The revised wandering controller. Because they require excitation from *LCF* to burst, the random bursters are now only active when the insect is actually walking. In addition, *LCS* has been made spontaneously active, so that the default behavior is wandering. Finally, a nonwandering command neuron (*NWC*) has been added so that higher precedence behaviors can prevent wandering when necessary.

8.5 Wandering Controller Revisions

Because the wandering controller is intended for exploration, it should only generate random turns when the insect is actually walking. This prevents the insect from turning in place. This can be accomplished by setting the thresholds of the random bursters so that their intrinsic currents alone are incapable of making them burst. *LCF* can then be used to provide the necessary excitation, ensuring that the random bursters generate turns only when the locomotion controller is active (Figure 8.3).

In order for wandering to be the default behavior for the insect, its controller must be active in the absence of activity in any of the other controllers. Given the interaction with locomotion discussed above, this implies that the locomotion controller must be spontaneously active. This can be accomplished by lowering the threshold of *LCS* such that it fires in

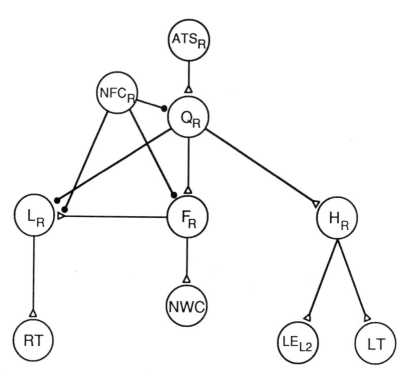

Figure 8.4: The revised edge-following controller. A nonfollowing command neuron (NFC) has been added so that higher precedence behaviors can disable edge-following on the right side of the body when necessary by inhibiting Q and F and gating the connection between F and L. In addition, an excitatory connection from F to NWC has been added in order to suppress wandering when edge-following is active. Similar revisions were made to the left edge-following controller.

approximately the middle of its range in the absence of any inputs.

Finally, controllers for higher priority behaviors must have some means for disabling wandering. Such a capability can be provided by adding a nonwandering command neuron (NWC) which overrides the excitation provided to the random bursters by LCS, effectively shutting off wandering when it is active (Figure 8.3).

8.6   Edge-Following Controller Revisions

Because edge-following takes precedence over wandering, the edge-following controllers must disable the wandering controller when edge-following is activated. As shown for the right edge-following controller in Figure 8.4, this can be accomplished through the addition of excitatory connections from F (which is active for the entire duration of the edge-following behavior) to the nonwandering command neuron NWC.

The edge-following controllers also need to be disabled by higher precedence behaviors. This can be accomplished by adding a nonfollowing command neuron (NFC) to each edge-controller as shown in Figure 8.4. When active, this neuron inhibits both Q and F. It also disables the connection between F and L. This gated synapse is necessary because of F's large capacitance, since F will continue to fire for some time even after it is inhibited.

We also need to consider the interaction between the edge-following controllers on each side of the body. For example, when the insect follows a right edge into a corner, the left tactile sensor will be stimulated and the left edge-following controller will activate. The insect cannot possibly follow two edges at once, so it must have some strategy for mediating the conflict between the two controllers. The strategy I have chosen is for the insect simply to reorient the antenna it was following with (in this case, the right one) to the new edge. As shown in Figure 8.5, this strategy can be implemented by adding a corner detection neuron (CR) to each edge-following controller. The CR neuron on a given side of the body is activated when the edge-following controller on the same side of the body is active and the antenna on the opposite side of the body contacts an edge. Once activated, it prevents the opposite edge-following controller from activating by exciting its NFC. It also generates a short turn away from the edge it was originally following. This will cause the antenna it was originally using for edge-following to contact the new edge and the normal reorientation

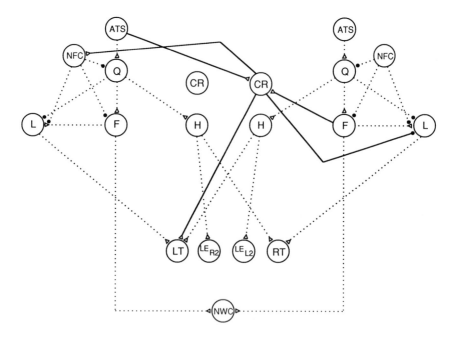

Figure 8.5: Interaction between the edge-following controllers on each side of the body. Connections comprising the individual edge-following controllers are shown with dotted lines. Only the connections underlying the interaction on the right side are shown with solid lines. The corresponding connections on the left side are omitted for clarity.

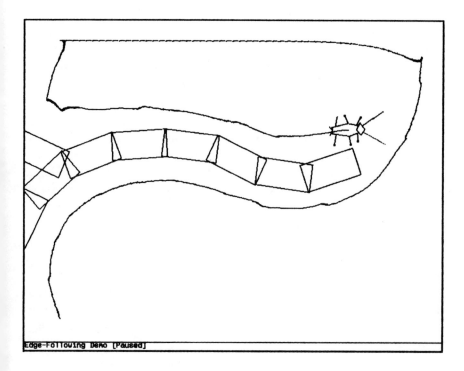

Edge-Following Demo [Paused]

Figure 8.6: The path of an insect following an edge around corners.

and following behavior for that side will ensue. This strategy is illustrated in Figure 8.6.

8.7 Feeding Controller Revisions

Because it is simpler, we will first consider the interactions between the consummatory controller and other behaviors. The revised consummatory controller is shown in Figure 8.7. Once an insect with a sufficiently high feeding arousal has contacted food, the consummatory command neuron (CC) is activated. In addition to actually releasing the consummatory behavior, this neuron must disable several other behaviors. It prevents any further locomotion by inhibiting the fast locomotion command neuron (LCF). It also disables wandering and edge-following by exciting the nonwandering (NWC) and nonfollowing (NFC) command neurons, respectively. Finally, it disables the appetitive controller by inhibiting the search command neuron (SC). If contact with food is lost during the course of feeding (e.g. because the food patch shrinks as it is consumed), this inhibition will disappear and, assuming that the insect is still sufficiently aroused, the appetitive controller will reactivate until contact is re-established.

The most complex behavioral interactions exhibited by *P. computatrix* involve the appetitive controller. Recall that the appetitive controller is designed to follow an odor gradient to food when the insect is sufficiently aroused to feeding. If it is following an odor, it must disable the wandering controller, which also utilizes the turning apparatus. However, if no odor signal is present, the insect may need to wander until a signal is found. Thus, the appetitive controller should disable the wandering controller only when it is actively following a signal. As shown in Figure 8.8, this can be implemented by adding a neuron which fires when the insect is actually following an odor (FO). This cell receives excitation from the search command neuron (SC) as well as both antennæ chemical sensors (ATS). Its threshold is arranged so that it only fires when SC is active and some odor is currently being registered by at least one of the ACS. When FO fires, it disables the wandering controller by exciting the nonwandering command neuron (NWC).

The interactions between the appetitive phase of feeding and edge-following are even more interesting. Normally, the appetitive phase should take precedence over edge-following. However, if an obstacle is encountered while following an odor gradient, the insect may need to edge-follow around it. This means that the relationship between the appetitive phase of feeding and edge-following is not strictly hierarchical, but depends upon the context. The key issue is whether or not the obstacle encountered lies between the insect and the food patch it is orienting to. To a first approximation, this is equivalent to determining whether or not the direction of greatest odor strength lies on the same side of the body as the obstacle encountered. If it does, the insect must edge-follow around the obstacle. If it does not, then the insect should suppress the edge-following behavior and continue to orient to the food patch.

This interaction is implemented as shown in Figure 8.9. Three new neurons have been added. FOL and FOR are active when the insect is following an odor whose strength is greater on the left or right side of its body, respectively. They operate by receiving excitation from the following

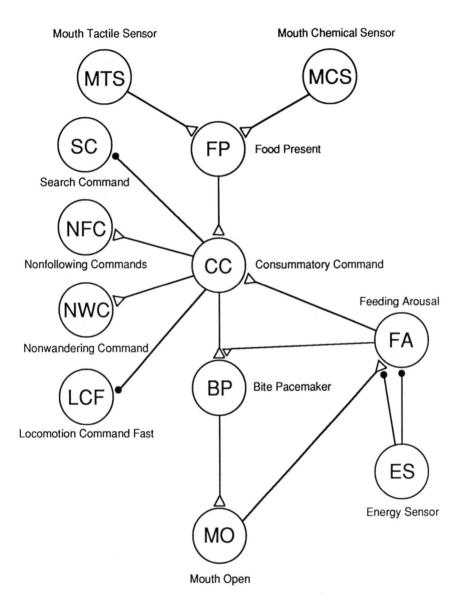

Figure 8.7: The revised consummatory controller. When biting is active, locomotion, wandering, edge-following, and appetitive behavior are suppressed.

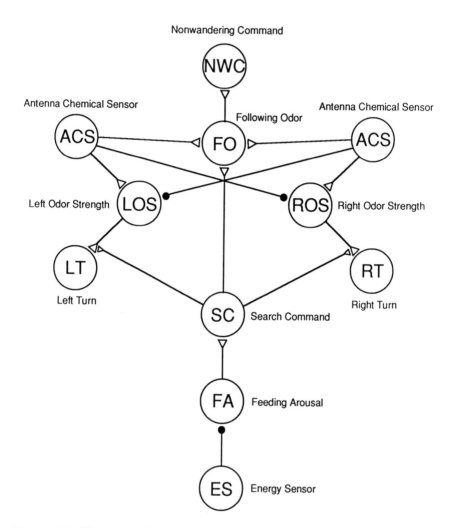

Figure 8.8: The appetitive controller revised for interaction with wandering. Wandering is disabled, via an inhibitory connection from FO to NWC, only when the insect is actually following an odor gradient. If no odor signal is present, or the insect is not sufficiently aroused to feeding, wandering is not affected.

odor neuron (FO) and the corresponding odor strength neuron (LOS or ROS). When FOL or FOR fires, it prevents edge-following on the opposite side of the body by exciting the opposite nonfollowing command neuron (NFC_R or NFC_L). Thus when the insect is following an odor whose source lies on one side of its body, it will not follow an edge on the opposite side of its body.

However, if an obstacle is encountered on the same side of the body as the odor source it is following, then the insect must edge-follow around the obstacle. In this case, the edge-following controller must temporarily prevent the appetitive controller from following the odor gradient as the insect follows the edge. As shown in Figure 8.9, this can be accomplished by interposing a new neuron, the following odor motor command neuron ($FOMC$), between the search command neuron and the connection of the odor following circuitry to the turn controller. This allows the left and right edge-following controllers to prevent odor following by simply inhibiting $FOMC$. Note, however, that SC remains active. Therefore, the appetitive controller has only partially ceded control to the edge-following controller. If conditions change (e.g. as the insect follows around the edge, the obstacle may no longer be in the path to food), the appetitive controller can immediately regain control.

As a foraging strategy, the above approach is far from perfect. For example, in certain situations it is possible for the insect to become trapped in an edge-following loop. However, as shown in the next section, the above strategy works reasonably well in most cases. It also demonstrates how nonhierarchical behavioral interactions can be implemented at the neural level. To improve the food finding performance of this insect, the implementation of more sophisticated foraging strategies should be considered (Kamil and Roitblat, 1985).

8.8 Results

The complete nervous system of *P. computatrix* contains 78 neurons and 156 connections. This nervous system implements the behavioral repertoire illustrated in Figure 8.1. This section briefly describes two examples which demonstrate this nervous system in operation, with particular emphasis on the behavioral interactions implemented in this chapter.

The first example shows the path of an insect over approximately 200 simulated seconds in an environment containing a patch of food (Fig-

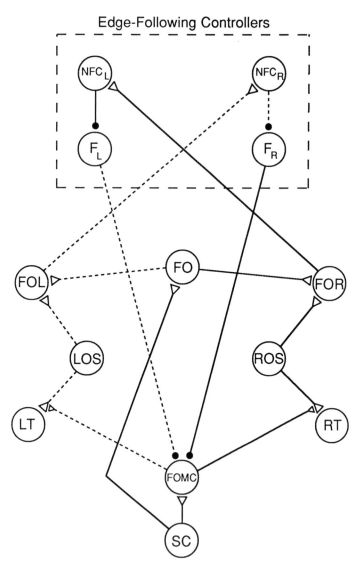

Figure 8.9: The appetitive controller revised for interaction with edge-following. Only those portions of the appetitive and edge-following controllers which are actually involved in the interaction are shown in detail. To further simplify the presentation, only those connections involving the right side of the appetitive controller are shown with solid lines. This side can suppress edge-following to the left, but can be suppressed by edge-following to the right. Refer to Figures 8.4 and 8.8 for context.

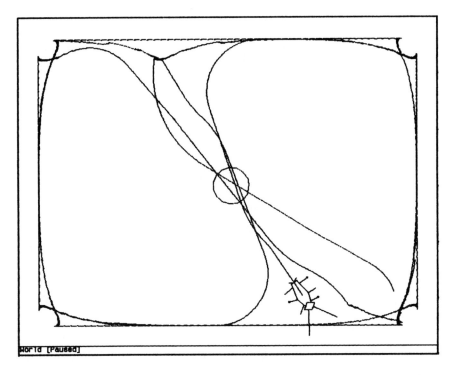

World [Paused]

Figure 8.10: The path of an insect during 200 simulated seconds exhibits periods of wandering, edge-following, and feeding.

ure 8.10). The insect's path exhibits periods of wandering, edge-following, and feeding. During this time, the insect fed four times (the insect's metabolism is rather high). Note that 200 seconds is much longer than this insect can survive without feeding. This insect is therefore demonstrating the capacity for an extended existence within its environment.

The second example shows how the interaction between its various behaviors is used to solve a simple problem in its environment (Figure 8.11). An insect is placed into a situation very similar to that shown in Figure 8.6, except that it has not been recently fed and a food patch is present in the environment. At (1), the insect is low on energy and immediately begins to locomote toward the food patch at the upper left under the control of the appetitive circuitry (note that obstacles do not block the diffusion of odor).

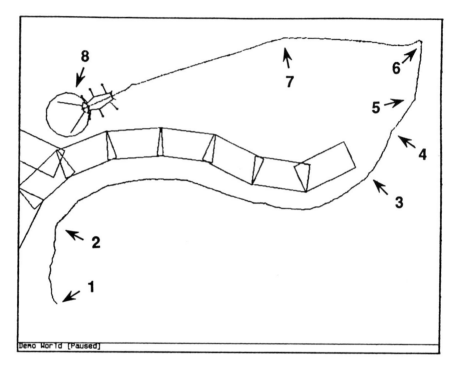

Figure 8.11: The path of an insect negotiating a simple maze.

At (2), however, it collides with the intervening wall and, since the wall lies
between the insect and food, begins to follow its edge. When the insect
loses contact with the wall at (3), it briefly tries to re-establish contact by
turning back toward it. When no further contact is forthcoming, the insect
begins to wander (4). Note that, due to the inverse square decay of odor
intensity with distance, the insect's chemosensors can no longer detect the
food patch at this point. After a short period of wandering, it collides with
the right wall at (5) and begins to follow it, negotiating a corner in the
process (6). As it continues to follow this edge, the insect once again comes
within range of the odor at (7). Because the edge it is currently following
does not block its path to food, it immediately leaves the wall and heads
toward the food patch, finally feeding successfully at (8).

Chapter 9

Discussion

9.1   Introduction

While it would certainly never be mistaken for a natural insect, *P. computatrix* nevertheless displays a number of interesting behavioral characteristics which are strikingly reminiscent of natural animals. It exhibits a variety of reflexes, taxes, and fixed-action patterns, along with rhythmic and motivated behavior and a behavioral hierarchy. The insect's behaviors include locomotion, wandering, edge-following, and feeding, and it is capable of flexibly organizing its behavioral repertoire in a variety of ways in order to meet the challenges posed by its environment. The insect is controlled by a heterogeneous artificial nervous system, which generates the patterns of behavior appropriate to the insect's situation without manipulating explicit representations of that situation. The artificial insect has therefore served well its role as an initial exploration into the feasibility of computational neuroethology. The remainder of this chapter discusses a number of broader issues which have been raised by this research.

9.2   Representation in *P. computatrix*

It is interesting to take a deeper look at the role that internal representations play in *P. computatrix*. Let us distinguish three different stances that one can take in explaining a system's behavior: (1) that of an external observer; (2) that of a designer; (3) that of the actual physical mechanisms responsible for the system's behavior. These stances are closely related to Dennett's intentional, design, and physical stances, respectively (Dennett, 1978a). They are also similar to distinctions that Clancey has drawn in an attempt to reconcile recent criticisms and proposals with more traditional approaches to AI (Clancey, 1989). The relationship between these three stances is usually quite straightforward for most engineered devices. This close correspondence is due to the nearly universal engineering methodology of successive refinement, in which the desired functionality is hierarchically decomposed into intermediate modules until some level is reached which is directly implementable in a physical substrate.

Now consider the behavior of the artificial insect from the perspective of an external observer. Even given the insect's extreme simplicity as compared to any natural animal, its behavior is sufficiently complex and organized to invite an intentional characterization. It is quite natural to speak of the insect as "looking" for food, or "trying" to get out of a corner or around an obstacle. It synthesizes quite rational "plans" of action for coping with nontrivial contingencies, such as the simple maze described in the previous chapter. Indeed, when it is sufficiently "hungry", its "desire" for food is sometimes striking, as it persistently strives to reach a food patch despite one's best attempts to thwart it (e.g. by repeatedly moving the food or the insect, or erecting barriers as it advances). There is simply no other way of characterizing this behavior than by attributing to the insect the internal goal of "wanting" to eat the food. It even exhibits varying degrees of "desire", ranging from "enthusiasm" when it has not fed for a considerable length of time, to "indifference" when it has recently completed a meal.

Beyond the usefulness of this intentional language, the artificial insect's interactions with its environment exhibit a great deal of structure and regularity, for which an observer could formulate a number of predictive laws or rules, such as the following:

1. If an insect moves quickly, it will adopt the tripod gait, while a slowly moving insect will exhibit distinct metachronal waves.

2. If a wandering insect encounters an obstacle, it will orient its body to the edge and follow it.

3. If an insect following an edge loses contact with it, it will attempt to re-establish contact for a short period of time and then give up.

4. If an insect has recently fed, it will be much less interested in any food that it encounters.

5. If a hungry insect which is following an odor field to food encounters an obstacle, it will follow its edge only if the obstacle lies between it and the food, otherwise it will ignore it.

I do not wish to make too much of the artificial insect's behavioral sophistication. More complex mazes for which the insect's simple strategies fail miserably can easily be constructed. In addition, it is not at all difficult to lay out symmetric arrangements of food patches which "trick" the insect into "believing" (falsely) that food exists where in fact it does not. My only point is that the insect's behavioral repertoire is nontrivial and highly organized. Furthermore, in many situations, this behavior appears quite rational given the insect's circumstances, and admits of a rich intentional characterization which invariably makes reference to entities internal to the insect. Indeed, it is quite possible that one could formulate a powerful theory of the insect's operation based entirely upon such a characterization.

Now consider *P. computatrix* from the perspective of a designer. Given the insect's body and environment, the sorts of behavioral regularities expressed above are clearly necessary to its survival. A designer must arrange the insect's nervous system so that it generates these behavioral regularities under the appropriate conditions. While symbolic descriptions of the insect's behavior can be quite useful and predictive, they abstract over many of the details of actually carrying out the behavior itself. For example, the action "orient to the edge and follow it" in the second rule above does not specify the actual leg movements required to accomplish this. The generation of these leg movements at the appropriate time is precisely the problem that must be solved by the insect in order to carry out the action described by the rule in the actual environment in which it is embedded. This is the problem that the neural circuitry responsible for edge-following is designed to solve. The artificial insect does not live in a symbolic world containing such entities as **IF wandering(Insect) & contact(Insect,Obstacle) THEN edge-follow(Insect,Obstacle)**, but rather one in which its legs, feet, and mouth must move in the appropriate ways at the appropriate times or it will die. The fact that an external observer finds the more abstract descriptions convenient is largely beside the point.

The interesting question, then, is how these external descriptions are related to the underlying neural mechanisms which are actually responsible for the insect's behavior. Therefore, let us consider the artificial insect from the perspective of its nervous system. Because its nervous system is not a general computational device, the most straightforward encoding of these descriptive regularities into symbolic rules is disallowed. Nevertheless, there are many cases in which the correspondence between a behavioral regularity which is succinctly captured by a rule and the underlying neural circuitry is fairly direct. For example, the switch between wandering and edge-following described by rule 2 above can be traced to specific neural mechanisms: the edge-following circuitry is activated when mechanical sensors in the antennae are stimulated, and this activity suppresses the wandering circuitry via one of two inhibitory connections (Figure 8.4). As a second, though considerably more complex, example, consider the implementation of rule 5 in the neural circuitry which mediates the context-dependent interaction between edge-following and the appetitive phase of feeding (Figure 8.9).

Identifying neural correlates for other behavioral regularities is considerably more problematic. For example, nowhere in the circuitry comprising the locomotion controller is there anything analogous to rule 1 above. Rather, the various gait patterns which are generated at different speeds of walking result from the dynamic interactions between the coupled pacemaker neurons and sensory feedback from the legs. As a second example, consider the complex internal dynamics underlying the insect's "desire" for food (Figure 7.7). Finally, consider the relatively constant exit angle of the recoil response (Figure 6.7), which derives from an invariant of the recoil controller's dynamics rather than any explicit rule. It is interesting to note that the most biologically-inspired controllers (i.e. those for locomotion and feeding) are the ones whose structure exhibits the least direct correspondence to externally perceived regularities. Imagine how much more difficult this relationship must be for a biological nervous system, whose structure bears the mark of no conscious designer.

Of course, there is nothing mysterious about the operation of the insect's nervous system. It is always possible to explain how its architecture and internal state organizes the insect's behavior in certain ways in certain circumstances. For example, knowing the current levels of activity in FA and ES, and the nature of their dynamics of interaction summarized in the phase plot of Figure 7.7, one could predict the insect's response to food at any given point in time. However, there is no standard sense of the notion of representation by which the artificial insect's nervous system can be said to represent many of the regularities that an external observer's intentional characterization attributes to it. Even the notion of *distributed representation* which is currently popular in connectionist networks does not really apply here, because it still suggests the existence of an internal representation which is simply spread over a number of units in some statistical sense rather than locally stored (Hinton *et al.*, 1986). The design of the artificial insect's nervous system is simply such that it generally synthesizes behavior that is appropriate to the insect's circumstances. This is precisely what I mean by structural congruence between an intelligent agent's internal dynamics and those of its external environment.

9.3 Goals and Reactive Responses

In the classical AI methodology, an intelligent agent's behavior derives from the execution of an internal plan, a step-by-step recipe of the individual actions to be performed. Prior to actually taking any action, this recipe is constructed by a planner from first principles based upon its knowledge of the agent's capabilities and a model of the world in which the agent operates. This view makes a number of crucial assumptions (Marks *et al.*, 1989):

1. The world will be stable; it will behave as projected.

2. Time consumed in planning is independent of the time that can be devoted to execution, so that the efficiency of the planner has no side-effects on the feasibility of the constructed plan.

3. The information available to the planner is complete, and execution will be flawless.

4. Any initially correct plan will remain correct and can in fact be carried out.

All of these assumptions are now widely held to be untenable for any intelligent agent which must interact with the real world. In addition, Chapman has shown that many aspects of classical planning are inherently combinatorially explosive, quickly becoming intractable for even simple real-world domains (Chapman, 1987). These problems have led to a number of recent attempts to make planning more responsive to the demands of realistic environments by relaxing the classical insistence on a strict separation between planning and execution.

One extreme is to abandon the planning phase altogether and remain continuously in the execution phase. This approach has produced systems which are purely reactive in the sense that they are always responding to the immediate situation in a reflex-like way (Agre and Chapman, 1987; Brooks, 1986; Firby, 1987; Kaelbling, 1986). However, such purely reactive systems are incapable of formulating and pursuing longer-term goals because they are always being pushed around by the world. This has led a number of researchers to propose various schemes for integrating reactive responses with more classical AI planning techniques which reason about explict internal models of the domain (Arkin, 1989; Turner, 1989; Georgeff and Lansky, 1987; Marks *et al.*, 1989).

The artificial insect suggests a third alternative. *P. computatrix* is clearly a reactive agent in the sense that its behavior is quite responsive to any contingencies which arise in its interactions with its environment. An insect which is tracking an odor signal to food, for example, switches immediately to edge-following behavior when it encounters an obstacle in its path. However, the artificial insect is not purely reactive, because it is also capable of organizing its individual behaviors in such a way as to achieve particular objectives. An insect which is hungry generates very different sequences of behavior than one which is not (e.g. Figure 7.4). Furthermore, as discussed above, this goal-oriented behavior is achieved without reasoning about an internal representation of the insect's situation. Rather, it derives from the ability of certain internal states of the insect's nervous system (e.g. those resulting from the interacting feedback loops underlying its feeding arousal) to modulate the interactions between the neural circuits responsible for its various behaviors.

Of course, the sort of goal-oriented problem-solving demonstrated in the artificial insect is currently rather limited. While it does exhibit, in one form or another, most of the behavioral characteristics discussed in Chapter 2, its repertoire is still quite impoverished as compared to that of any natural animal. In addition to locomotion, wandering, edge-following, and feeding, insect behavior includes escape responses, fighting, nest building, foraging, grooming, mating, and communication. The neural implementation of more sophisticated behavioral repertoires should certainly be explored, both in insects and other simpler animals. Unfortunately, though there is a rich body of literature on the ethology of such behaviors, there is very little currently known about the underlying neural circuitry. Ultimately, it would be interesting to have several species of artificial animals interacting and evolving within a simulated environment.

Even if such a rich repertoire of behavior were added to the artificial insect, it would still suffer from a number of serious limitations from the classical AI perspective: it maintains no internal models of the world, engages in no deliberative reasoning, and exhibits no general problem-solving abilities. In short, it does none of the things which are typically expected of an AI system. Instead, *P. computatrix* contains a special-purpose nervous system which endows it with a rich but fixed behavioral repertoire. I have not ignored such uniquely human capabilities as language and conscious reasoning because I think them unimportant. On the contrary, I believe that they are among the most fascinating phenomena of this or any other field. However, an early point of departure of the work described in this book was that our sophisticated cognitive abilities derive from successive elaborations of the more basic competence, shared with all natural animals, for flexibly coping with the world, and are fundamentally inseperable from it.

There is an assumption, popular among philosophers, that the brain processes that make for cognition are one sort of thing and that the brain processes that contribute to motor control belong to an entirely different category. Accordingly, the assumption may be used to justify a disregard of research on motor control by those doing research on cognition. But if we look at matters from an evolutionary and neurobiological point of view, the assumption is not only naive, it in fact trammels the theoretical imagination. It is like trying to do physics on the assumption that one set of laws and principles applies to the sublunary sphere, and a quite different set to the superlunary sphere.

Higher functions are surely not discontinuous with lower functions; they are not a sphere unto themselves. Needless to say, this does *not* mean that psychological investigations of perception, memory, and the like, are therefore inappropriate. [...] But it does mean that if we want to understand the fundamental principles of cognition, we may need to understand the emergence in evolution of those paradigmatically cognitive processes, and hence we may need to understand their origins in sensorimotor control. It does mean, therefore, that a principled disregard of sensorimotor control by philosophers may deprive them of just the perspective needed to understand the fundamental principles underlying intelligent behavior. (Churchland, 1986, p. 451)

9.4   Heterogeneous Neural Networks

Work in the area of artificial neural networks has typically made use of uniform collections of simple units interconnected in some regular architecture, such as layered feedforward or fully interconnected. These homogeneous networks are usually trained by a general learning procedure to perform a desired task. Such networks have interesting computational properties and can often be rapidly configured to perform difficult tasks with immediate practical applications. However, because these networks begin with essentially no information concerning the nature of the task they are to perform, a disproportionately large burden is placed upon the learning procedure. This is a burden the learning algorithm is not always well-equipped to handle. There is a growing body of both empirical and theoretical evidence that suggests that the kind of learning practiced in artificial neural networks is intractable in general (e.g. Blum and Rivest, 1989).

In contrast, nervous systems are extremely heterogeneous. Individual nerve cells possess complex intrinsic dynamics which endow them with often unique response properties. The activity of a nerve cell at any point in time is a function not only of the activity of the other nerve cells which synapse on it, but also its shape, the characteristics and distribution of its current channels, its chemical environment, and its internal biochemical state (Selverston, 1988; Llinás, 1988; Bullock, 1976). In addition, the patterns of connection between nerve cells are far from uniform. Nervous systems consist of many individual circuits which are organized into complicated but highly specific designs. Nervous systems result from developmental processes which have been shaped by millions of years of evolution to produce architectures uniquely suited to controlling the behavior of the animals in which they are embedded. Far from being unimportant biological details, much of this heterogeneity appears to be crucial to the operation of nervous systems, and the source of much of their power. For this reason, there has been a growing demand for more biologically-realistic neural models and architectures in artificial neural networks (Crick, 1989; Selverston, 1988; DARPA, 1988).

The neural controllers developed in this book represent one small step in this direction. In designing the nervous system of the artificial insect, I have shown how certain kinds of biological heterogeneity can be incorporated into artificial neural networks. The neural model employed in this book captures some of the intrinsic properties of nerve cells through the inclusion of intrinsic currents. These currents have been used to produce model pacemakers, trigger neurons, and random bursters. In addition, such neurobiological concepts as reflexes, central pattern generators modulated by sensory feedback, entrainment between coupled oscillators, command neurons, multifunctionality, interacting positive and negative feedback loops, and distributed decision-making circuits have been explored. Some of the most biologically-inspired controllers (e.g. those for locomotion and feeding arousal maintenance) have demonstrated an impressive dynamical richness.

Unfortunately, much of the artificial insect's nervous system is rather *ad hoc*. While some portions of it are based directly upon neurobiological data, many other parts were hand-designed. Even the biologically-inspired controllers had to be fine-tuned by trial and error (there are over 500 parameters in the artificial insect's nervous system!). I would have preferred a more principled approach to these issues, but the required neurobiological data was often simply not available. Because I was interested in designing a complete autonomous agent rather than modeling only isolated pieces of behavior, I was forced to fill in many missing details. As much as possible, I tried to do this in a "neurobiologically plausible" way. Only further study of natural nervous systems and considerably more design experience with artificial ones will increase the sophistication of these designs, and deepen the principles upon which they are based. The artificial insect has demonstrated at least one way in which a number of principles of nervous system organization can be utilized to control the behavior of an autonomous agent. With further experience, it may eventually be possible to abstract more universal design principles for artificial nervous systems. However, these design principles may be of a very different sort than those typically practiced in the classical engineering methodology.

The artificial insect also currently exhibits no plasticity of any sort. While it is capable of flexibly synthesizing behavior appropriate to its circumstances, it cannot modify this ability to take into account its past experiences. Learning is obviously a terribly important feature of intelligent behavior, but it plays no direct causal role in the actual generation of a particular behavior in a particular situation. It is this capacity for adaptive behavior which has been the focus of concern in this book. Rather, learning is one of the processes by which behavior becomes adaptive in the first place, and remains so throughout an animal's life. As dicussed in Chapter 2, there are a number of neural mechanisms which are known or hypothesized to underlie behavioral plasticity in simpler animals. The incorporation of such mechanisms into artificial nervous systems should certainly be explored. It would also be interesting to study development and evolution in order to understand the processes which produce the appropriate structural congruence between nervous systems and the bodies and environments in which they are embedded.

Finally, one of the advantages of the simpler models currently employed in artificial neural networks is that they are analytically tractable; one can often prove theorems about their behavior. As more biologically-realistic models and architectures are explored, it becomes considerably more difficult to analyze their behavior. In Chapter 5, I have shown that the neurobiological technique of lesion studies can give considerable insight into the operation of a heterogeneous neural network, as well as testing its robustness to various perturbations. While a lesion study cannot replace a mathematical analysis, it can help to focus it and to interpret its results.

9.5   Neurobiological Implications

It is interesting to note that some aspects of the artificial insect's nervous system have potential neurobiological significance. The locomotion controller, for example, has illustrated the strengths and weaknesses of a proposed neurobiological model for cockroach locomotion, and suggested a plausible extension. With this addition, the artificial insect exhibits most of the full range of known insect gaits simply by varying the activity level of a single command neuron. In addition, the results from several lesion experiments on this controller are similar to those observed in natural insects. The lesion study may also shed some light on the difficulty of resolving the current neurobiological controversey regarding the relative roles of central and peripheral components in pattern generation. Finally, the feeding controller demonstrates that the mechanisms hypothesized to underlie feeding arousal and satiation in *Aplysia* are capable of producing interbite interval graphs which bear a strong qualitative resemblance to those actually observed.

I believe that, constrained by the appropriate biological data, simulations of the sort described here could potentially be very powerful tools for the neuroethological modeling of actual biological systems. A neuroethological model would directly inherit all of the advantages offered by the computer modeling of neural circuitry. However, most modeling work in computational neuroscience seeks to reproduce, either quantitatively or qualitatively, only various aspects of nerve cells (typically firing frequency or membrane potential trajectories). If we are interested in the neural control of behavior, it is not at all clear that we can ignore the body in which the nervous system is embedded. It is this body which connects its nervous system to behavior, and, as we have even seen in lesion studies of the simulated insect, sensory feedback from the body can subtly shape the dynamics of a neural controller in ways which are crucial to its normal functioning.

For example, the neural circuitry controlling the leg of an insect does not generate simple "forward", "reverse", and "turn" signals. Rather, it is designed to generate control signals appropriate to the specific structure of the leg and the dozens of muscles which are attached to it. The global effect of the contraction of some muscle at a given point in time may be strongly context dependent. In addition, reflex effects and intrinsic body dynamics, which the nervous system may take full advantage of, involve the body in a fundamental way in the movements which a given pattern of neural activity actually produce. There is a strong tendency to think of sensorimotor control as a master/slave system in which the body faithfully responds to the commands of the nervous system. However, a more accurate picture is probably one in which the neural circuitry and body form two complex systems, each with their own intrinsic dynamics, which are coupled in such a way as to produce the appropriate behavior. The behavior resulting from such a tightly coupled system can only be fully understood by a neuroethological approach which seeks to model both the underlying neural circuitry and the relevant aspects of the body and environment in which it is embedded.

9.6 Autonomous Robots

There is currently a great deal of interest in the design of autonomous robots. Most current robots must be told precisely what to do, and what not do do, often in excruciating detail. These low-level instructions are tedious to write, and leave the robot vulnerable to contingencies which, though unanticipated by the programmer, cannot be ignored in any real-world environment. At the very least, a robot should be capable of coping with minor surprises which arise in the execution of its instructions, e.g. reflexively avoiding an unanticipated obstacle which crosses its prepro-grammed path. Ideally, it should be possible to instill robots with more general objectives, such as "keep this area clean," rather than explicitly specifying the movement of individual joints. The actual details of satisfy-ing such goals in a given environment would then be handled by the robot itself.

Many of the problems confronted by a robot which must function for extended periods of time without human intervention, such as a robot for extraterrestrial exploration, are quite similar to the ones that simpler ani-mals such as insects have already solved. The behavior of such a robot must be goal-oriented, adaptive, opportunistic, plastic, and robust. It must be capable of flexibly adapting its behavior to a variety of unforeseen contin-gencies without direct human intervention. These are the very problems for which nervous systems were designed. I am therefore interested in constructing autonomous robots which are controlled by artificial nervous systems whose design has been abstracted from biological nervous systems. It would seem that neural controllers such as those developed in this book may be of direct use for the control of autonomous robots. For example, the neural controller for walking in *P. computatrix* could serve as the basis for a very fast, robust, and distributed locomotion controller for a legged robot. Brooks has had some notable successes with building robots capable of a number of simple autonomous behaviors (Brooks, 1989; Brooks, 1986; Connell, 1987; Horswill and Brooks, 1988). I believe that a more biological approach might add an interesting perspective to this endeavor.

9.7   Conclusion

Throughout this book, I have emphasized two themes which are at odds with accepted AI doctrine: (1) that studying the adaptive behavior of sim-pler animals can teach us fundamental lessons about human cognition, and (2) that understanding the biological mechanisms underlying this behavior is essential. I do not undertake such heresy lightly. However, a careful con-sideration of the limitations of current AI systems has led me to question some of the presuppositions underlying the classical AI methodology.

The AI perspective on simpler animals is perhaps best illustrated by Simon's parable of the ant on the beach (Simon, 1969, pp. 63-65). Simon holds that the complicated behavior of an ant meandering along a beach is more a function of the complexity of the beach than the ant. But given what is now known about the neuroethology of simpler animals, some of which has been illustrated here in *P. computatrix*, this is clearly only half the picture. Certainly the environment is complex, *but so is the ant.* Simpler animals are not simple, and not just in the trivial sense that they are physically complex. Even the marine mollusc *Aplysia*, an invertebrate with six orders of magnitude fewer nerve cells than are found in the human brain, exhibits a variety of motivated behaviors, as well as various forms of nonassociative and associative learning. More importantly, an *Aplysia* is capable of utilizing its limited behavioral repertoire to successfully cope with the unforeseen contingencies which are characteristic of the real world in which it must survive. It is this fundamental capability for adaptive behavior, exhibited by even the simplest animals, which AI systems uniformly lack.

As for the biological details, the neural mechanisms underlying the behavior of natural animals have not played any significant role in artificial intelligence research. In defense of this fact, people in AI are fond of quoting the old adage that airplanes do not need feathers in order to fly. But both birds and airplanes do have wings and, more importantly, they both depend upon Bernoulli's principle to defeat the common tug of gravity. It is easy in hindsight to distinguish the critical characteristics from the inessential ones.[1] But it seems to me the epitome of hubris to believe that we can understand or design systems which exhibit so complex a set of phenomena as constitute intelligence without even once bothering to peek inside the working examples which surround us. "Theorists almost always assume that they are cleverer than natural selection. This is usually a mistake." (Crick and Asanuma, 1986, p. 369).

---

[1] However, even the example of flight may not be as clear-cut as it seems. As pointed out to me by Hillel Chiel, many more biological details of the construction of a bird wing may very well be essential if one wished to build a device that could take off from and land on a branch.

Appendix A

Physical Parameters

This appendix gives further details concerning the physical model employed in the book. As for a natural animal, the body of *P. computatrix*, and the environment in which it is embedded, have important consequences for the design of its nervous system. The precise layout of the body model is shown in Figure A.1. In this same coordinate system, the lengths of the legs are 17, 15, and 17 for the front, middle, and back legs, respectively. This is the length assumed by the leg when its foot is up. A leg whose foot is down stretches between the foot and the body. A foot changes state instantaneously.

The angle limits of each leg are $[\pi/5, 0]$, $[\pi/12, -\pi/12]$, and $[\pi/12, -\pi/8]$ radians for the front, middle and back legs, respectively. By convention, the angle of a leg which is perpendicular to the body is 0, and positive angles lie in the clockwise direction for legs on the left side of the body and in the counterclockwise direction for legs on the right side of the body. Note that a leg whose foot is down may bend past these limits. Once the foot of such a leg goes up, its angle will be restored to the proper range if it has bent too far forward, but not if it has bent too far back.

The "center of mass" of the body lies at the origin of the coordinate axes shown in Figure A.1. The static stability of the body is assessed by determining whether or not this center of mass lies within the polygon of support formed by the feet which are down. If it does not, the body begins to fall. If static stability has not been restored within 40 msec, the insect is treated as if it has fallen down and the legs are no longer able to move the body.

By swinging when its foot is down, a leg can apply a force parallel to the body which serves to translate the body either forward or back. In addition, legs can apply lateral forces perpendicular to the body which serve to both rotate and translate it. The maximum parallel force that a single leg can apply is 50. The maximum lateral force that a leg can apply is 7. The constant of proportionality (which I have rather loosely referred to as "mass") between the velocity of an insect and the "force" applied to it is 100. The corresponding constant of proportionality between angular velocity and "torque" is 5000.

Every physical time step (20 msec), the insect uses up .25 units of energy. *P. computatrix* has an energy storage capacity of 1000 units. Energy units are obtained from food patches whose energy capacity is equal to their area. Every time an insect opens and closes its mouth over a food patch, 25 units of energy are transferred from the food patch to the insect. Food patches also emit an odor whose strength is equal to the energy capacity of the food patch. These odors diffuse through the environment, decreasing in intensity as the inverse square of the distance from the center of the food patch.

An insect can collide with the walls which form the edge of the screen or with rectangular bricks in its environment. For the purposes of collisions, only the tips of the antennae and cerci of an insect are considered. A collision is detected when one of these four points crosses into a wall or brick from one physical time step to the next. When this happens, the insect is backed up to the point where the actual contact occurred and a small bounce of one pixel is added in a direction perpendicular to the edge contacted.

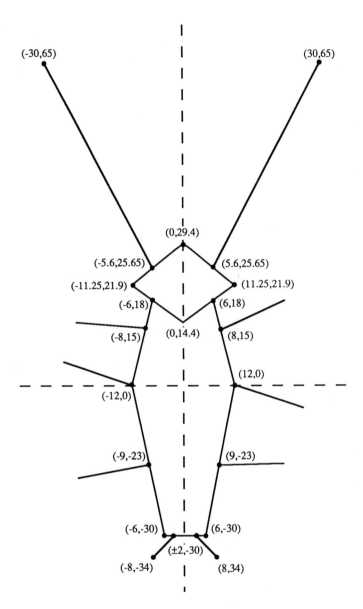

Figure A.1: The precise layout of the body model.

Appendix B

Neural Parameters

This appendix gives all of the neural parameters associated with the controllers described in the book. It is important to realize that these values are by no means unique. Nevertheless, this appendix makes precise the more qualitative descriptions employed in the main text.

Every model neuron has at least five parameters associated with it: membrane conductance (denoted by $G_{membrane}$), membrane capacitance (denoted by $C_{membrane}$), minimum firing frequency (denoted by F_{min}), threshold voltage (denoted by $V_{threshold}$), and gain. Very few neurons have a nonzero F_{min}, so it will usually be omitted.

More complex model neurons may have additional parameters. Pacemakers and random bursters have two intrinsic currents (called High and Low) whose magnitude (denoted I_L and I_H, respectively) and duration (denoted T_L and T_H, respectively) are given. A trigger neuron has a single intrinsic current (called Trigger) whose magnitude (denoted I_T) and duration (denoted T_T) are given. Functions which give the duration of an intrinsic current are specified in terms of $V_\infty(t)$, which is the steady-state voltage that the membrane would reach if the total input current at time t were held constant. In addition, sensory neurons have an intrinsic current (denoted $I_{sensory}$) whose magnitude is a function of the intensity of some physical quantity, and motor neurons have an effector function which maps its firing frequency to some physical quantity.

A connection from neuron A to neuron B is denoted $A \rightarrow B$, and its weight is given in nA. A compound connection in which neuron C synapses

177

on a connection from A to B is denoted $C \rightarrow (A \rightarrow B)$. Compound synapses may be either gating or modulatory. A gating compound synapse also has an ungated state associated with it.

The order of presentation of controllers in this appendix follows that of the main text. In general, this appendix contains a section for each circuit or group of closely related circuits. For clarity, the relevant sections and figures are referenced. More than one version of some of the controllers have been presented in this book, and only the changes from an earlier version are shown for a subsequent one.

B.1 Leg Controller

(Section 4.3, Figure 4.2)

Recall that there are six copies of this controller, one for each leg, except that the command neuron LC is shared by all of the leg controllers.

Neuron LC

$G_{membrane}$: .1 μS
$C_{membrane}$: 75 μF
$V_{threshold}$: $-3\ mV$
F_{min} : .25
$Gain$: .1 mV^{-1}

Pacemaker Neuron P

$G_{membrane}$: .5 μS
$C_{membrane}$: 10 μF
$V_{threshold}$: 10 mV
$Gain$: .1 mV^{-1}
I_L : $-10\ nA$
I_H : 20 nA
T_L : **if** $V_\infty(t) > -20\ mV$ **then** $-31.25V_\infty(t) + 175\ msec$ **else** ∞
T_H : 75 $msec$

Motor Neuron *Stance*

$G_{membrane}$: .5 μS

$C_{membrane}$: 10 μF
$V_{threshold}$: 0 mV
$Gain$: .1 mV^{-1}
Backward Leg Swing Force : $firing\_frequency * maximum\_leg\_force$

Motor Neuron *Swing*

$G_{membrane}$: .5 μS
$C_{membrane}$: 10 μF
$V_{threshold}$: 0 mV
$Gain$: .1 mV^{-1}
Forward Leg Swing Force : $firing\_frequency * maximum\_leg\_force$

Motor Neuron *Foot*

$G_{membrane}$: .5 μS
$C_{membrane}$: 10 μF
$V_{threshold}$: -2 mV
$Gain$: 1 mV^{-1}
Foot State : **if** $firing\_frequency > 0$ **then** *foot_down* **else** *foot_up*

Sensory Neuron *Backward Angle Sensor*

$G_{membrane}$: .5 μS
$C_{membrane}$: 5 μF
$V_{threshold}$: 5 mV
$Gain$: 1 mV^{-1}
$I_{sensory}$: **if** $leg\_angle \leq minimum\_leg\_angle$ **then** 10 nA **else** 0 nA

Sensory Neuron *Forward Angle Sensor*

$G_{membrane}$: .5 μS
$C_{membrane}$: 5 μF
$V_{threshold}$: 5 mV
$Gain$: 1 mV^{-1}
$I_{sensory}$: **if** $leg\_angle \geq maximum\_leg\_angle$ **then** 10 nA **else** 0 nA

Connections

$LC \rightarrow Stance$: 5 nA

$LC \rightarrow P :$ 10 nA
$P \rightarrow Stance :$ -10 nA
$P \rightarrow Swing :$ 10 nA
$P \rightarrow Foot :$ -4 nA
Backward Angle Sensor $\rightarrow P :$ 10 nA
Forward Angle Sensor $\rightarrow P :$ -15 nA
Forward Angle Sensor $\rightarrow Stance :$ 10nA
Forward Angle Sensor $\rightarrow Swing :$ -15 nA
Forward Angle Sensor $\rightarrow Foot :$ 10 nA

B.2   Locomotion Controller

(Section 4.4, Figure 4.3)

Connections

$P_{L1} \rightarrow P_{R1} :$ -15 nA
$P_{R1} \rightarrow P_{L1} :$ -15 nA
$P_{L2} \rightarrow P_{R2} :$ -15 nA
$P_{R2} \rightarrow P_{L2} :$ -15 nA
$P_{L3} \rightarrow P_{R3} :$ -15 nA
$P_{R3} \rightarrow P_{L3} :$ -15 nA
$P_{L1} \rightarrow P_{L2} :$ -15 nA
$P_{L2} \rightarrow P_{L1} :$ -15 nA
$P_{L2} \rightarrow P_{L3} :$ -15 nA
$P_{L3} \rightarrow P_{L2} :$ -15 nA
$P_{R1} \rightarrow P_{R2} :$ -15 nA
$P_{R2} \rightarrow P_{R1} :$ -15 nA
$P_{R2} \rightarrow P_{R3} :$ -15 nA
$P_{R3} \rightarrow P_{R2} :$ -15 nA

B.3   Turning Controller

(Section 6.2, Figure 6.1)

Motor Neurons LE_{L1} and LE_{R1}

$G_{membrane} :$ .5 μS
$C_{membrane} :$ 10 μF

$V_{threshold}$: 0 mV
$Gain$: .1 mV^{-1}
Leg Lateral Force : *firing_frequency* ∗ *maximum_leg_lateral_force*

Neurons RT and LT

$G_{membrane}$: .5 μS
$C_{membrane}$: 10 μF
$V_{threshold}$: 0 mV
$Gain$: 1 mV^{-1}

Connections

$LT \rightarrow LE_{R1}$: 5 nA
$RT \rightarrow LE_{L1}$: 5 nA
$LT \rightarrow RT$: −10 nA
$RT \rightarrow LT$: −10 nA

B.4 Wandering Controller

(Section 6.3, Figure 6.2)

The wandering controller builds upon the turning controller above.

Random Burster Neurons RB_L and RB_R

$G_{membrane}$: .5 μS
$C_{membrane}$: 10 μF
$V_{threshold}$: 10 mV
$Gain$: .1 mV^{-1}
I_L : −10 nA
I_H : 2 nA
T_L : *Uniformly distributed in the range* [2000, 3000] *msec*
T_H : *Uniformly distributed in the range* [500, 3500] *msec*

Connections

$RB_R \rightarrow LT$: 3.5 nA
$RB_L \rightarrow RT$: 3.5 nA

B.5   Backward Locomotion Controller

(Section 6.4, Figure 6.4)

The backward locomotion controller adds connections to the forward locomotion controller, as well as gating synapses from a backward locomotion command neuron which select between these two sets of connections. Recall that the backward locomotion controller, and the recoil controller below which utilizes it, were not included in the final insect. Also note that, in order to minimize the number of extra connections required, many of the forward locomotion connections are reused for backward locomotion by using gating synapses to invert their sign rather than simply disable them. This detail was glossed over in the main text and in Figure 6.4.

Neuron BC

$G_{membrane}$: $.5\ \mu S$
$C_{membrane}$: $10\ \mu F$
$V_{threshold}$: $0\ mV$
$Gain$: $1\ mV^{-1}$

Connections

(Note that the forward and backward angle sensors have been abbreviated FAS and BAS, respectively)

$LC \rightarrow Swing$: $5\ nA$
$BAS \rightarrow Stance$: $10\ nA$
$BAS \rightarrow Swing$: $-15\ nA$
$BAS \rightarrow Foot$: $10\ nA$
$BC \rightarrow (FAS \rightarrow P)$: $-2\ nA$ {Gated Synapse, Ungated State = 1}
$BC \rightarrow (FAS \rightarrow Stance)$: $-1\ nA$ {Gated Synapse, Ungated State = 1}
$BC \rightarrow (FAS \rightarrow Swing)$: $-1\ nA$ {Gated Synapse, Ungated State = 1}
$BC \rightarrow (FAS \rightarrow Foot)$: $-1\ nA$ {Gated Synapse, Ungated State = 1}
$BC \rightarrow (BAS \rightarrow P)$: $-2\ nA$ {Gated Synapse, Ungated State = 1}
$BC \rightarrow (LC \rightarrow Stance)$: $-1\ nA$ {Gated Synapse, Ungated State = 1}
$BC \rightarrow (P \rightarrow Stance)$: $-2\ nA$ {Gated Synapse, Ungated State = 1}
$BC \rightarrow (P \rightarrow Swing)$: $-2\ nA$ {Gated Synapse, Ungated State = 1}
$BC \rightarrow (BAS \rightarrow Stance)$: $1\ nA$ {Gated Synapse, Ungated State = 0}

$BC \rightarrow (BAS \rightarrow Swing) : 1\ nA$ {*Gated Synapse, Ungated State* $= 0$}
$BC \rightarrow (BAS \rightarrow Foot) : 1\ nA$ {*Gated Synapse, Ungated State* $= 0$}
$BC \rightarrow (LC \rightarrow Swing) : 1\ nA$ {*Gated Synapse, Ungated State* $= 0$}

B.6   Recoil Controller

(Section 6.4, Figure 6.6)

Recall that the recoil controller was not a part of the final insect. Also note that there are two copies of this controller, one for each antenna.

Sensory Neuron ATS

$G_{membrane}$: .5 μS
$C_{membrane}$: 5 μF
$V_{threshold}$: 0 mV
$Gain$: .1 mV^{-1}
$I_{sensory}$: **if** *antenna_contact* **then** $16/\pi * contact\_angle$ nA **else** 0 nA

Trigger Neuron A

$G_{membrane}$: .5 μS
$C_{membrane}$: 10 μF
$V_{threshold}$: .1 mV
$Gain$: .1 mV^{-1}
I_T : **if** *antenna_contact* **then** $16/\pi * contact\_angle$ nA **else** 0 nA
T_T : $200V_\infty(t) + 500$ *msec*

Neuron B

$G_{membrane}$: .5 μS
$C_{membrane}$: 25 μF
$V_{threshold}$: 0 mV
$Gain$: 1 mV^{-1}

Neuron C

$G_{membrane}$: .5 μS
$C_{membrane}$: 400 μF

$V_{threshold}$: 10 mV
$Gain$: 1 mV^{-1}

Neuron D

$G_{membrane}$: .5 μS
$C_{membrane}$: 300 μF
$V_{threshold}$: 15 mV
$Gain$: 1 mV^{-1}

Neuron E

$G_{membrane}$: .5 μS
$C_{membrane}$: 10 μF
$V_{threshold}$: 4 mV
$Gain$: 2 mV^{-1}

Connections

$ATS \rightarrow A$: 5 nA
$A \rightarrow B$: 10 nA
$A \rightarrow C$: −4 nA
$A \rightarrow E$: 5 nA
$B \rightarrow LT$: 4 nA   {*For right antenna*}
$B \rightarrow RT$: 4 nA   {*For left antenna*}
$C \rightarrow D$: 10 nA
$C \rightarrow E$: −7 nA
$D \rightarrow A$: −15 nA
$D \rightarrow B$: −15 nA
$E \rightarrow BC$: 5 nA

B.7 Edge-Following Controller

(Section 6.5, Figure 6.8)

Note that there are two copies of this controller, one for each antenna.

Sensory Neuron ATS

$G_{membrane}$: .5 μS
$C_{membrane}$: 5 μF
$V_{threshold}$: 0 mV
$Gain$: .1 mV^{-1}
$I_{sensory}$: **if** antenna_contact **then** $16/\pi * contact\_angle$ nA
for **max**(contact_duration, 500) $msec$ **else** 0 nA

Neuron Q

$G_{membrane}$: .5 μS
$C_{membrane}$: 15 μF
$V_{threshold}$: 0 mV
$Gain$: .5 mV^{-1}

Neuron L

$G_{membrane}$: .5 μS
$C_{membrane}$: 10 μF
$V_{threshold}$: 0 mV
$Gain$: 1 mV^{-1}

Neuron F

$G_{membrane}$: .5 μS
$C_{membrane}$: 200 μF
$V_{threshold}$: 0 mV
$Gain$: 10 mV^{-1}

Neuron H

$G_{membrane}$: .5 μS
$C_{membrane}$: 10 μF
$V_{threshold}$: 1 mV
$Gain$: .1 mV^{-1}

Motor Neuron LE

$G_{membrane}$: .5 μS
$C_{membrane}$: 10 μF

$V_{threshold}$: 0 mV
$Gain$: .1 mV^{-1}
$Leg\ Lateral\ Force$: $firing\_frequency * maximum\_leg\_lateral\_force$

Connections

$ATS \rightarrow Q$: 1 nA
$Q \rightarrow L$: −15 nA
$Q \rightarrow F$: 5 nA
$Q \rightarrow H$: 6 nA
$L \rightarrow RT$: 6 nA   {*For right antenna*}
$L \rightarrow LT$: 6 nA   {*For left antenna*}
$F \rightarrow L$: 1 nA
$H \rightarrow LE_{L2}$: 2 nA   {*For right antenna*}
$H \rightarrow LE_{R2}$: 2 nA   {*For left antenna*}
$H \rightarrow LT$: 3.5 nA   {*For right antenna*}
$H \rightarrow RT$: 3.5 nA   {*For left antenna*}

B.8   Appetitive Controller

(Section 7.3, Figure 7.1)

Sensory Neurons ACS_L and ACS_R

$G_{membrane}$: .5 μS
$C_{membrane}$: 10 μF
$V_{threshold}$: 0 mV
$Gain$: 10 mV^{-1}
$I_{sensory}$: .1 * $odor\_strength$ − .0025 nA

Sensory Neuron ES

$G_{membrane}$: .5 μS
$C_{membrane}$: 10 μF
$V_{threshold}$: 0 mV
$Gain$: .1 mV^{-1}
$I_{sensory}$: 5/$energy\_capacity$ nA

Neurons *LOS* and *ROS*

$G_{membrane}$: .5 μS
$C_{membrane}$: 10 μF
$V_{threshold}$: 0 mV
$Gain$: 10 mV^{-1}

Neuron *FA*

$G_{membrane}$: .5 μS
$C_{membrane}$: 300 μF
$V_{threshold}$: -8 mV
$Gain$: .1 mV^{-1}

Neuron *SC*

$G_{membrane}$: .5 μS
$C_{membrane}$: 10 μF
$Vthreshold$: 2 mV
$Gain$: 1 mV^{-1}

Connections

$ACS_L \rightarrow LOS$: 5 nA
$ACS_L \rightarrow ROS$: -5 nA
$ACS_R \rightarrow LOS$: -5 nA
$ACS_R \rightarrow ROS$: 5 nA
$LOS \rightarrow LT$: 1 nA
$ROS \rightarrow RT$: 1 nA
$ES \rightarrow FA$: -5 nA
$FA \rightarrow SC$: 5 nA
$SC \rightarrow (LOS \rightarrow LT)$: 5 nA {*Gated Synapse, Ungated State* = 0}
$SC \rightarrow (ROS \rightarrow RT)$: 5 nA {*Gated Synapse, Ungated State* = 0}

B.9 Consummatory Controller

(Section 7.4, Figure 7.2)

Sensory Neuron MTS

$G_{membrane}$: .5 μS
$C_{membrane}$: 10 μF
$V_{threshold}$: 0 mV
$Gain$: 1 mV^{-1}
$I_{sensory}$: **if** $mouth\_contact$ **then** 5 nA **else** 0 nA

Sensory Neuron MCS

$G_{membrane}$: .5 μS
$C_{membrane}$: 10 μF
$V_{threshold}$: 0 mV
$Gain$: 1 mV^{-1}
$I_{sensory}$: .05 $*$ $odor\_strength$ $-$ .05 nA

Motor Neuron MO

$G_{membrane}$: .5 μS
$C_{membrane}$: 10 μF
$V_{threshold}$: 0 mV
$Gain$: 1 mV^{-1}
$Mouth\ State$: **if** $firing\_frequency$ > .5 **then** $mouth\_open$ **else** $mouth\_closed$

Neuron FP

$G_{membrane}$: .5 μS
$C_{membrane}$: 10 μF
$V_{threshold}$: 10.1 mV
$Gain$: 2 mV^{-1}

Neuron CC

$G_{membrane}$: .5 μS
$C_{membrane}$: 10 μF
$V_{threshold}$: 10.1 mV
$Gain$: 2 mV^{-1}

Pacemaker Neuron BP

$G_{membrane}$: .5 μS
$C_{membrane}$: 10 μF
$V_{threshold}$: 10 mV
$Gain$: .1 mV^{-1}
I_L : -10 nA
I_H : 20 nA
T_L : **if** $V_\infty(t) > -21$ mV **then** $-14.77V_\infty(t) + 104$ $msec$ **else** ∞
T_H : 50 $msec$

Connections

$MT \rightarrow FP$: 5 nA
$MCS \rightarrow FP$: 15 nA
$FP \rightarrow CC$: 5 nA
$FA \rightarrow CC$: 5 nA
$CC \rightarrow BP$: 1 nA
$BP \rightarrow MO$: 5 nA
$MO \rightarrow FA$: 15 nA
$FA \rightarrow (CC \rightarrow BP)$: 9 nA {*Modulatory Synapse*}
$ES \rightarrow (MO \rightarrow FA)$: -1.5 nA {*Modulatory Synapse*}

B.10   Locomotion Controller Revisions

(Section 8.4, Figure 8.2)

Neuron LCS

$G_{membrane}$: .1 μS
$C_{membrane}$: 75 μF
$V_{threshold}$: -3.1 mV
F_{min} : .35
$Gain$: .1 mV^{-1}

Neuron LCF

$G_{membrane}$: .5 μS
$C_{membrane}$: 10 μF

$V_{threshold}$: 0 mV
$Gain$: 1 mV^{-1}

Connections

$LCS \rightarrow LCF$: .5 nA
$LCF \rightarrow Stance$: 5 nA
$LCF \rightarrow P$: 10 nA

B.11   Wandering Controller Revisions

(Section 8.5, Figure 8.3)

Neuron NWC

$G_{membrane}$: .5 μS
$C_{membrane}$: 10 μF
$V_{threshold}$: 1 mV
$Gain$: 1 mV^{-1}

Connections

$LCF \rightarrow RB_L$: 10 nA
$LCF \rightarrow RB_R$: 10 nA
$NWC \rightarrow RB_L$: -15 nA
$NWC \rightarrow RB_R$: -15 nA

B.12   Edge-Following Controller Revisions

(Section 8.6, Figures 8.4 and 8.5)

Neurons NFC_L and NFC_R

$G_{membrane}$: .5 μS
$C_{membrane}$: 10 μF
$V_{threshold}$: 0 mV
$Gain$: 1 mV^{-1}

Neurons CR_L and CR_R

$G_{membrane}$: .5 μS
$C_{membrane}$: 10 μF
$V_{threshold}$: 0 mV
$Gain$: 1 mV^{-1}

Connections

$NFC_L \rightarrow Q_L$: $-2\ nA$
$NFC_R \rightarrow Q_R$: $-2\ nA$
$NFC_L \rightarrow F_L$: $-5\ nA$
$NFC_R \rightarrow F_R$: $-5\ nA$
$NFC_L \rightarrow (F_L \rightarrow L_L)$: $-1\ nA$ {*Gated Synapse, Ungated State* = 1}
$NFC_R \rightarrow (F_R \rightarrow L_R)$: $-1\ nA$ {*Gated Synapse, Ungated State* = 1}
$ATS_L \rightarrow C_R$: 3 nA
$ATS_R \rightarrow C_L$: 3 nA
$F_L \rightarrow C_L$: 3 nA
$F_R \rightarrow C_R$: 3 nA
$C_L \rightarrow NFC_R$: 5 nA
$C_R \rightarrow NFC_L$: 5 nA
$C_L \rightarrow L_L$: $-2\ nA$
$C_R \rightarrow L_R$: $-2\ nA$
$C_L \rightarrow R_T$: 5 nA
$C_R \rightarrow L_T$: 5 nA

B.13   Consummatory Controller Revisions

(Section 8.7, Figure 8.7)

Connections

$CC \rightarrow LCF$: $-5\ nA$
$CC \rightarrow NWC$: 10 nA
$CC \rightarrow SC$: $-7\ nA$
$CC \rightarrow NFC_L$: 5 nA
$CC \rightarrow NFC_R$: 5 nA

B.14   Appetitive Controller Revisions

(Section 8.7, Figures 8.8 and 8.9)

Neuron FO

$G_{membrane}$: .5 muS
$C_{membrane}$: 10 μF
$V_{threshold}$: 10.001 mV
$Gain$: 2 mV^{-1}

Neurons FO_L and FO_R

$G_{membrane}$: .5 μS
$C_{membrane}$: 10 μF
$V_{threshold}$: 10.1 mV
$Gain$: 10 mV^{-1}

Neuron $FOMC$

$G_{membrane}$: .5 μS
$C_{membrane}$: 10 μF
$V_{threshold}$: 0 mV
$Gain$: 2 mV^{-1}

Connections

$ACS_L \rightarrow FO$: 4 nA
$ACS_R \rightarrow FO$: 4 nA
$SC \rightarrow FO$: 5 nA
$FO \rightarrow NWC$: 10 nA
$FO \rightarrow FOL$: 5 nA
$FO \rightarrow FOR$: 5 nA
$LOS \rightarrow FOL$: 4 nA
$ROS \rightarrow FOR$: 4 nA
$FOL \rightarrow NFC_R$: 5 nA
$FOR \rightarrow NFC_L$: 5 nA
$F_L \rightarrow FOMC$: -5 nA
$F_R \rightarrow FOMC$: -5 nA
$SC \rightarrow FOMC$: 5 nA

$FOMC \rightarrow (LOS \rightarrow LT) :\ 5\ nA$ {*Gated Synapse, Ungated State* $= 0$}
$FOMC \rightarrow (ROS \rightarrow RT) :\ 5\ nA$ {*Gated Synapse, Ungated State* $= 0$}

Bibliography

Agre, P.E. (1988). *The Dynamic Structure of Everyday Life*. Technical Report AI-TR-1085, Artificial Intelligence Laboratory, MIT, Cambridge, MA.

Agre, P. and Chapman, D. (1987). Pengi: An implementation of a theory of activity. In *Proceedings of AAAI-87* (pp. 268-272).

Altman, J. (1989). Deceptively simple behaviour. *Nature* **242**:481-482.

Altman, J.S. and Kien, J. (1987). A model for decision making in the insect nervous system. In M.A. Ali (Ed.), *Nervous Systems in Invertebrates* (pp. 621-643). New York: Plenum Press.

Altman, J.S. and Kien, J. (1989). New models for motor control. *Neural Computation* **1**:173-183.

Arbib, M.A. (1982). *Rana computatrix*: An evolving model of visuomotor coordination in frog and toad. In J.E. Hayes, D. Michie and Y.H. Pao (Eds.), *Machine Intelligence 10*. Ellis Horwood.

Arbib, M.A. (1987). Levels of modeling of mechanisms of visually guided behavior. *Behavioral and Brain Sciences* **10**:407-465.

Arkin, R.C. (1989). Motor schema-based mobile robot navigation. *The International Journal of Robotics Research* **8**(4):92-112.

Baerends, G.P., Brouwer, R. and Waterbolk, H.T.J. (1955). Ethological studies on *Lebistes reticulatus* (Peters). I. Analysis of the male courtship pattern. *Behaviour* 8:249-334.

Bell, W.J. and Adiyodi, K.G. (1981). *The American Cockroach*. New York: Chapman and Hall.

Berreman, G. (1946). Anemic and emetic analyses in social anthropology. *American Anthropologist* 68(2):346-354.

Bierre, P. (1985). The professor's challenge. *AI Magazine* 5(4):60-70.

Blum, A. and Rivest, R.L. (1989). Training a 3-node neural network is NP-complete. In D.S. Touretzky (Ed.), *Advances in Neural Information Processing Systems I* (pp. 494-501). San Mateo, CA: Morgon Kaufman Publishers.

Booker, L.B. (1988). Classifier systems that learn internal world models. *Machine Learning* 3:161-192.

Braitenberg, V. (1984). *Vehicles: Experiments in Synthetic Psychology*. Cambridge, MA: MIT Press.

Borg-Graham, L.J. (1988). Modeling the electrical behavior of cortical neurons - simulation of hippocampal pyramidal cells. In R.J. Cotterill (Ed.), *Computer Simulation in Brain Science* (pp. 384-404). Cambridge University Press.

Brooks, R.A. (1986). A robust layered control system for a mobile robot. *IEEE Journal of Robotics and Automation* **RA-2**(1):14-23.

Brooks, R.A. (1987). Intelligence without representation. Unpublished paper, MIT AI Lab.

Brooks, R.A. (1989). A robot that walks: Emergent behaviors from a carefully evolved network. *Neural Computation* 1(2):253-262.

Bullock, T.H. (1976). In search of principles in neural integration. In J.C. Fentress (Ed.), *Simpler Networks and Behavior* (pp. 52-60). Sunderland, MA: Sinauer.

Byrne, J.H. and Gingrich, K.J. (1989). Mathematical model of cellular and molecular processes contributing to associative and nonassociative learning in *Aplysia*. In J.H. Byrne and W.O. Berry (Eds.) *Neural Models of Plasticity*. Academic Press.

Camhi, J.M. (1984). *Neuroethology*. Sunderland, MA: Sinauer Associates.

Carew, T.J. (1985). The control of reflex action. In E.R. Kandel and J.H. Schwartz (Eds.), *Principles of Neural Science* (pp. 457-468). New York: Elsevier.

Chapman, D. (1987). Planning for conjunctive goals. *Artificial Intelligence* **32**(3):333-377.

Churchland, P.S. (1986). *Neurophilosophy*. Cambridge, MA: MIT Press.

Churchland, P.S. and Sejnowski, T.J. (1988). Perspectives on cognitive neuroscience. *Science* **242**:741-745.

Clancey, W.J. (1989). The frame of reference problem in cognitive modeling. In *Proc. of the Eleventh Annual Conf. of the Cognitive Science Society* (pp. 107-114).

Coderre, B. (1988). Modeling behavior in Petworld. In C. Langton (Ed.), *Artificial Life*. Addison-Wesley Publishing Company.

Connell, J.H. (1987). Creature design with the subsumption architecture. In *Proceedings of AAAI-87* (pp. 1124-1126).

Crick, F. (1989). The recent excitement about neural networks. *Nature* **337**:129-132.

Crick, F. and Asanuma, C. (1986). Certain aspects of the anatomy and physiology of the cerebral cortex. In D.E. Rumelhart and J.L. McClelland (Eds.), *Parallel Distributed Processing, Vol. 1* (pp. 333-371). Cambridge, MA: MIT Press.

DARPA (1988). *DARPA Neural Network Study*. AFCEA Press.

Delcomyn, F. (1971). The locomotion of the cockroach *Periplaneta americana*. *J. Exp. Biol.* **54**:443-452.

Delcomyn, F. (1980). Neural basis of rhythmic behavior in animals. *Science* **210**:492-498.

Dennett, D.C. (1978a). Intentional systems. In *Brainstorms*. Cambridge, MA: MIT Press.

Dennett, D.C. (1978b). Why not the whole iguana? *Behavioral and Brain Sciences* **1**:103-104.

Dennett, D.C. (1986). The logical geography of computational approaches: A view from the east pole. In M. Brand and R.M. Harnish (Eds.), *The Representation of Knowledge and Belief.* Tuscon, AZ: University of Arizona Press.

Dennett, D.C. (1987). Intentional systems in cognitive ethology: The "Panglossian Paradigm" defended, in *The Intentional Stance.* Cambridge, MA: MIT Press.

Donner, M. (1987). *Real-time Control of Walking (Progress in Computer Science, Vol. 7).* Cambridge, MA: Birkhauser Boston, Inc.

Dreyfus, H.L. (1979). *What Computers Can't Do.* New York: Harper and Row.

Dreyfus, H.L. and Dreyfus, S.E. (1988). Making a mind versus modeling the brain: AI back at a branchpoint. *Dædalus* **117**(1):15-43.

Durbin, R. and Rumelhart, D.E. (1989). Product units: A computationally powerful and biologically plausible extension to backpropagation networks. *Neural Computation* **1**(1):133-142.

Edelman, G.M. (1987). *Neural Darwinism.* New York: Basic Books.

Firby, R.J. (1987). An investigation into reative planning in complex domains. In *Proceedings of AAAI-87* (pp. 202-206).

Fodor, J.A. (1975). *The Language of Thought.* Cambridge, MA: Harvard University Press.

Garcia, J., Hankins, W.G. and Rusiniak, K.W. (1974). Behavioral regulation of the milieu interne in man and rat. *Science* **185**:824-831.

Gardner, H. (1983). *Frames of Mind: The Theory of Multiple Intelligences.* New York: Basic Books.

Gardner, H. (1985). *The Mind's New Science: A History of the Cognitive Revolution.* New York: Basic Books.

Garfinkel, H. (1967). *Studies in Ethnomethodology.* Englewood Cliffs, NJ: Prentice-Hall.

Georgeff, M.P. and Lansky, A.L. (1987). Reactive reasoning and planning. In *Proceedings of AAAI-87* (pp. 677-682).

Getting, P.A. (1989). Reconstruction of small neural networks. In C. Koch and I. Segev (Eds.), *Methods in Neuronal Modeling*. Cambridge, MA: MIT Press.

Getting, P.A. and Dekin, M.S. (1985). Tritonia swimming: A model system for integration within rhythmic motor systems. In A.I. Selverston (Ed.), *Model Neural Networks and Behavior* (pp. 3-20). New York: Plenum Press.

Gladwin, T. (1964). Culture and logical process. In W. Goodenough (Ed.), *Explorations in Cultural Anthropology: Essays Presented to George Peter Murdick*. New York: McGraw-Hill.

Graham, D. (1977). Simulation of a model for the coordination of leg movement in free walking insects. *Biological Cybernetics* **26**:187-198.

Graham, D. (1985). Pattern and control of walking in insects. *Advances in Insect Physiology* **18**:31-140.

Grillner, S. (1981). Control of locomotion in bipeds, tetrapods, and fish. In V.B. Brooks (Ed.), *The Handbook of Physiology, Sect. 1, Vol. 2, The Nervous System, Motor Control* (pp. 1179-1236). Am. Physiol. Soc. Maryland: Waverly Press.

Grossberg, S., ed. (1988). *Neural Networks and Natural Intelligence*. Cambridge, MA: MIT Press.

Harris-Warrick, R.M. and Johnson, B.R. (1989). Motor pattern networks: Flexible foundations for rhythmic pattern production. In T.J. Carew and D.B. Kelley (Eds.), *Perspectives in Neural Systems and Behavior*. New York: Alan R. Liss.

Hartline, D.K. (1979). Pattern generation in the lobster (Panulirus) stomatogastric ganglion II: Pyloric network simulation. *Biological Cybernetics* **33**:223-236.

Heidegger, M. (1962). *Being and Time*. New York: Harper and Row.

Heritage, J. (1984). *Garfinkel and Ethnomethodology*. Cambridge, England: Policy Press.

Hillis, W. D. (1985). *The Connection Machine.* Cambridge, MA: MIT Press.

Hinton, G.E. (1987). Connectionist learning procedures. Technical Report CMU-CS-87-115, Computer Science Dept., Carnegie-Mellon University.

Hinton, G.E., McClelland, J.L. and Rumelhart, D.E. (1986). Distributed representations. In D.E. Rumelhart and J.L. McClelland (Eds.), *Parallel Distributed Processing, Vol. 1* (pp. 77-109). Cambridge, MA: MIT Press.

Hobbs, J. and Moore, R.C., eds (1985). *Formal Theories of the Commonsense World.* Ablex Publishing.

Hodgkin, A.L. and Huxley, A.F. (1952). A quantitative description of membrane current and its application to conduction and excitation in nerve. *J. Physiol.* (London) **117**:500-544.

Hood, G. (1985). Neural modeling as one approach to machine learning. In *Proceedings of the Third International Machine Learning Workshop,* Skytop, PA.

Hood, G. (1986). Artificial organisms: A neural modeling approach. Thesis proposal, Computer Science Dept., Carnegie-Mellon University.

Hood, G. and Carbonell, J.G. (1982). The world modelers project: Constructing a simulated environment to aid AI research. In *Proceedings of the 13th Annual Conference on Modeling and Simulation* (pp. 669-673).

Hopfield, J.J. (1982). Neural networks and physical systems with emergent collective computational abilities. *Proc. Natl. Acad. Sci. (USA)* **79**:2554-2558.

Hopfield, J.J. (1984). Neurons with graded responses have collective computational properties like those of two-state neurons. *Proc. Natl. Acad. Sci.* **81**:3088-3092.

Hopfield, J.J. and Tank, D.W. (1985). Neural computation of decisions in optimization problems. *Biological Cybernetics* **52**:141-152.

Horswill, I.D. and Brooks, R.D. (1988). Situated vision in a dynamic world: chasing objects. In *Proceedings of AAAI-88* (pp. 796-800).

Kaelbling, L. (1987). An architecture for intelligent reactive systems. In *Proceedings of the 1986 Workshop on Reasoning about Actions and Plans* (pp. 395-410). Morgan Kaufmann Publishers.

Kamil, A.C and Roitblat, H.L (1985). The ecology of foraging behavior: Implications for animal learning and memory. *Annual Review of Psychology* 36:141-169.

Kandel, E.R. (1976). *Cellular Basis of Behavior.* San Francisco: W.H. Freeman.

Kandel, E.R. (1985). Cellular mechanisms of learning and the biological basis of individuality. In E.R. Kandel and J.H. Schwartz (Eds.), *Principles of Neural Science* (pp. 816-833). New York: Elsevier.

Kandel, E.R. and Schwartz, J.H. (1985). *Principles of Neural Science.* New York: Elsevier.

Koch, C. and Segev, I. (1989). *Methods in Neuronal Modeling.* Cambridge, MA: MIT Press.

Koch, C., Poggio, T., and Torre, V. (1983). Nonlinear interaction in a dendritic tree: Localization, timing and role in information processing. *Proc. Natl. Acad. Sci. USA* 80:2799-2802.

Kovac, M. (1974). Abdominal movements during backward walking in the crayfish. II. The neuronal basis. *J. Comp. Physiol.* 95:71-94.

Kristan, W., Lockery, S., Wittenberg, G. and Cottrell, G.W. (1989). Behavioral choice - In theory and practice. In R. Durbin, C. Miall, and G. Mitchison (Eds.), *The Computing Neuron* (pp. 180-204). Addison-Wesley.

Kupfermann, I.J. (1974). Feeding behavior in *Aplysia*: A simple system for the study of motivation. *Behavioral Biology* 10:1-26.

Kupfermann, I.J. and Weiss, K.R. (1978). The command neuron concept. *Behavioral and Brain Sciences* 1:3-39.

Lakoff, G. (1987). *Women, Fire, and Dangerous Things.* Chicago: The University of Chicago Press.

Lenat, D., Prakash, M., Shepard, M. (1986). CYC: Using commonsense knowledge to overcome brittleness and knowledge acquisition bottlenecks. *AI Magazine* **6**(4):65-85.

Llinás, R.R. (1988). The intrinsic electrophysiological properties of mammalian neurons: Insights into central nervous system function. *Science* **242**:1654-1664.

Llinás, R.R. (1989). *The Biology of the Brain*. New York: W.H. Freeman.

Lorenz, K.Z. (1981). *The Foundations of Ethology*. New York: Simon and Schuster.

Maes, P. (1989). The dynamics of action selection. In *Proceedings of the Eleventh International Joint Conference on AI* (IJCAI 89) (pp. 991-997). Morgan Kaufmann Publishers.

Marks, M., Hammond, K. and Converse, T. (1989). Planning in an open world: A pluralistic approach. In *Proceedings of AAAI-87* (pp. 749-756).

Maturana, H.R. and Varela, F.J. (1980). *Autopoiesis and Cognition (Boston Studies in the Philosophy of Science, Volume 42)*. Boston, MA: D. Reidel Publishing Company.

Maturana, H.R. and Varela, F.J. (1987). *The Tree of Knowledge*. Boston, MA: Shambhala Press.

McCarthy, J. (1988). Mathematical logic in artificial intelligence. *Dædalus* **117**(1):297-311.

McClelland, J.L. (1986). Resource requirements of standard and programmable nets, In D.E. Rumelhart and J.L. McClelland (Eds.), *Parallel Distributed Processing, Vol. 1* (pp. 460-487). Cambridge, MA: MIT Press.

McClelland, J.L. and Rumelhart, D.E. (1986). *Parallel Distributed Processing, Vol. 2: Psychological and Biological Models*. Cambridge, MA: MIT Press.

McCullough, W.S. and Pitts, W.H. (1943). A logical calculus of the ideas immanent in nervous activity. *Bulletin of Mathematical Biophysics* **5**:115-133.

McDermott, D. (1987). A critque of pure reason. *Computational Intelligence* **3**:151-160.

McKenna, M.A. and Zeltzer, D. (1989). Dynamic simulation of autonomous legged locomotion. Unpublished paper, MIT Media Lab.

Minsky, M. (1985). *The Society of Mind.* New York: Simon and Schuster.

Murphey, R.K. and Zaretsky, M.D. (1972). Orientation to calling song by female crickets, *Scapsipedus marginatus(Gryllidae). J. Exp. Biol.* **56**:335-352.

Newell, A. and Simon, H.A. (1976). Computer science as empirical inquiry: Symbols and search. *Communications of the ACM* **19**(3):113-126.

Pao, Y.H. (1989). *Adaptive Pattern Recognition and Neural Networks.* Addison-Wesley.

Payton, D. (1986). An architecture for reflexive autonomous vehicle control. In *Proc. IEEE Conf. on Robotics and Auto.* (pp. 1838-1845).

Pearson, K.G. (1976a). The control of walking. *Scientific American* **235**:72-86.

Pearson, K.G. (1976b). Nerve cells without action potentials. In J.C. Fentress (Ed.), *Simpler Networks and Behavior* (pp. 99-110). Sunderland, MA: Sinauer Associates.

Pearson, K.G. (1985). Are there central pattern generators for walking and flight in insects? In W.J.P. Barnes and M.H. Gladden (Eds.), *Feedback and Motor Control in Invertebrates and Vertebrates* (pp. 307-315). London: Croom Helm.

Pearson, K.G., Fourtner, C.R. and Wong, R.K. (1973). Nervous control of walking in the cockroach. In R.B. Stein, K.G. Pearson, R.S. Smith, and J.B. Redford (Eds.), *Control of Posture and Locomotion* (pp. 495-514). Plenum Press.

Pylyshyn, Z.W. (1984). *Computation and Cognition.* Cambridge, MA: MIT Press.

Pylyshyn, Z.W. and Demopoulos, W. (1986). *Meaning and Cognitive Structure.* Norwood, NJ: Ablex Publishing Corp.

Raibert, M. H. (1989). *Legged Robots That Balance.* Cambridge, MA: MIT Press.

Rall, W. (1977). Core conductor theory and cable properties of neurons. In J.M. Brookhart, V.B. Mountcastle, and E.R. Kandel (Eds.), *Handbook of Physiology, Vol. 1, Pt. 1, The Nervous System, Cellular Biology of Neurons.* (pp. 39-97). Bethesda, MD: American Physiological Society.

Ramirez, J.M. and Pearson, K.G. (1988). Generation of motor patterns for walking and flight in motoneurons supplying bifunctional muscles in the locust. *J. Neurobiology* 19:257-282.

Reed, S.K. (1982). *Cognition: Theory and Applications.* Monterey, CA: Brooks/Cole Publishing Co.

Reeke, G. N. Jr. and Edelman, G.M. (1988). Real brains and artificial intelligence. *Dædalus* 117(1):143-173.

Ritzmann, R.E. (1984). The cockroach escape response. In R.C. Eaton (Ed.), *Neural Mechanisms of Startle Behavior* (pp. 93-131). New York: Plenum Press.

Rizki, M.M. and Conrad, M. (1986). Computing the theory of evolution. *Physica* 22D:83-99.

Rorty, R. (1979). *Philosophy and the Mirror of Nature.* Princeton, NJ: Princeton University Press.

Rowell, C.H.F., Reichert, H. and Bacon, J.P. (1985). How Locusts fly straight. In W.J.P. Barnes and M.H. Gladden (Eds.), *Feedback and Motor Control in Invertebrates and Vertebrates* (pp. 337-354). London: Croom Helm.

Rumelhart, D.E. and McClelland, J.L. (1986). *Parallel Distributed Processing, Vol. 1: Foundations.* Cambridge, MA: MIT Press.

Rumelhart, D.E., Hinton, G.E. and McClelland, J.L. (1986). A general framework for parallel distributed processing. In D.E. Rumelhart and J.L. McClelland (Eds.), *Parallel Distributed Processing, Vol. 1.* (pp. 45-76). Cambridge, MA: MIT Press.

Rumelhart, D.E., Hinton, G.E. and Williams, R.J. (1986). Learning internal representations by error propagation. In D.E. Rumelhart and

J.L. McClelland (Eds.), *Parallel Distributed Processing, Vol. 1.* (pp. 318-362). Cambridge, MA: MIT Press.

Schneirla, T.C. (1953). Basic problems in the nature of insect behavior. In K.D. Roeder (Ed.), *Insect Physiology* (pp. 656-684). New York: Wiley.

Schöner, G. and Kelso, J.A.S. (1988). Dynamic pattern generation in behavioral and neural systems. *Science* **239**:1513-1520.

Sejnowski, T.J. and Rosenberg, C.R. (1987). Parallel networks that learn to pronounce English text. *Complex Systems* **1**:145-168.

Sejnowski, T.J., Koch, C., and Churchland, P.S. (1988). Computational neuroscience. *Science* **241**:1299-1306.

Selverston, A.I. (1988). A consideration of invertebrate central pattern generators as computational data bases. *Neural Networks* **1**(2):109-117.

Shepherd, G.M. (1988). *Neurobiology.* New York: Oxford University Press.

Simon, H. (1969). *The Sciences of the Artificial.* Cambridge, MA: MIT Press.

Song, S., and Waldron, K. (1989). *Machines That Walk: The Adaptive Suspension Vehicle.* Cambridge, MA: MIT Press.

Smith, B.C. (1985). Prologue to "Reflection and Semantics in a Procedural Language," In R.J. Brachman and H.J. Levesque (Eds.), *Readings in Knowledge Representation.* Los Altos, CA: Morgan Kaufmann Publishers.

Spitzer, N.C. (1982). *Neuronal Development.* Plenum Press.

Stefik, M. and Bobrow, D.G. (1987). Misunderstanding computers and cognition, Book Review of *Understanding Computers and Cognition,* by T. Winograd and F. Flores. *Artificial Intelligence* **31**(2):220- 226.

Sternberg, R.J. (1985). *Beyond IQ: A Triarchic Theory of Human Intelligence.* Cambridge University Press.

Sternberg, R.J. and Wagner, R.K. (1986). *Practical Intelligence.* Cambridge University Press.

Stich, S.P. (1983). *From Folk Psychology to Cognitive Science*. Cambridge, MA: MIT Press.

Stillings, N.A., Feinstein, M.H., Garfield, J.L., Rissland, E.L., Rosenbaum, D.A., Weisler, S.E. and Baker-Ward, L. (1987). *Cognitive Science*. Cambridge, MA: MIT Press.

Suchman, L.A. (1987). *Plans and Situated Actions*. Cambridge University Press.

Susswein, A.J., Weiss, K.R. and Kupfermann, I. (1978). The effects of food arousal on the latency of biting in *Aplysia*. *J. Comp. Physiol.* **123**:31-41.

Taylor, C.E., Jefferson, D.R., Turner, S.R. and Goldman, S.R. (1988). RAM: Artificial life for the exploration of complex biological systems. In C. Langton (Ed.), *Artificial Life*. Addison-Wesley.

Todd, D. J. (1985), *Walking Machines: An Introduction to Legged Robots*. Kogan Page.

Traub, R.D., Miles, R., and Wong, R.K.S. (1989). Model of the origin of rhythmic population oscillations in the hippocampal slice. *Science* **243**:1319-1325.

Travers, M. (1988a). Animal construction kits. In C. Langton (Ed.), *Artificial Life*. Addison-Wesley Publishing Company.

Travers, M. (1988b). *Agar: An Animal Construction Kit*. M.S. Thesis, MIT Media Lab.

Turner, R.M. (1989). When reactive planning is not enough: Using contextual schemas to react appropriately to environmental change. In *Proc. of the Eleventh Annual Conf. of the Cognitive Science Society* (pp. 940-947).

Varela, F.J. (1979). *Principles of Biological Autonomy*. New York: Elsevier North Holland.

Walter, W.G. (1950). An imitation of life. *Scientific American*, May, 1950, pp. 42-45.

Walter, W.G. (1953). *The Living Brain*. Duckworth.

Waltz, D.L. (1988). The prospects for building truly intelligent machines. *Dædalus* **117**(1):191-212.

Watson, A.H.D. and Burrows, M. (1985). The synaptic basis for integration of local reflexes in the Locust. In W.J.P. Barnes and M.H. Gladden (Eds.), *Feedback and Motor Control in Invertebrates and Vertebrates* (pp. 231-250). London: Croom Helm.

Weinreb, D. and Moon, D. (1980). Flavors: Message passing in the Lisp machine. AI Memo 602, Artificial Intelligence Laboratory, Massachesetts Institute of Technology, Cambridge, MA.

Weiss, K.R., Chiel, H.J., Koch, U. and Kupfermann, I. (1986). Activity of an identified histaminergic neuron, and its possible role in arousal of feeding behavior in semi-intact *Aplysia*. *J. Neuroscience* **6**(8):2403-2415.

Weiss, K.R., Chiel, H.J. and Kupfermann, I. (1986). Sensory function and gating of histaminergic neuron C2 in *Aplysia*. *J. Neuroscience* **6**(8):2416-2426.

Wilson, D.M. (1966). Insect walking. *Annual Review of Entomology* **11**:103-122.

Wilson, M.A. and Bower, J.M. (1989). The simulation of large-scale neural networks. In C. Koch and I. Segev (Eds.), *Methods in Neuronal Modeling*. Cambridge, MA: MIT Press.

Wilson, S.W. (1985). Knowledge growth in an artificial animal. In *Proceedings of the First International Conference on Genetic Algorithms* (pp. 16-23). Pittsburgh, PA: Lawrence Erlbaum.

Wilson, S.W. (1987). Classifier systems and the animat problem. *Machine Learning* **2**:199-228.

Winograd, T. (1985). Moving the semantic fulcrum. *Linguistics and Philosophy* **8**(1):91-104.

Winograd, T. (1987a). Is realism for real? *CSLI Monthly* **2**(5):1-5.

Winograd, T. (1987b). Thinking machines: Can there be? Are we? Technical Report CSLI-87-100, Center for the Study of Language and Information, Stanford University.

Winograd, T. (1987c). Logic isn't the problem. *Computational Intelligence* **3**:221-222.

Winograd, T. and Flores, F. (1986). *Understanding Computers and Cognition: A New Foundation for Design.* Norwood, NJ: Ablex Publishing Corporation.

Wong, R.K.S and Pearson, K.G. (1976). Properties of the trochanteral hair plate and its function in the control of walking in the cockroach. *J. Exp. Biol.* **64**:233-249.

Zill, S. (1985). Proprioceptive feedback and the control of cockroach walking. In W.J.P. Barnes and M.H. Gladden (Eds.), *Feedback and Motor Control in Invertebrates and Vertebrates* (pp. 187-208). London: Croom Helm.

Index

Perspectives in
Artificial
Intelligence